cGRAW-HILL READING

Grammar

rade 6

Practice Book

McGraw-Hill
School Division
ork Farmington

CONTENTS

GRADE 6/UNIT 3: With Flying Colors

Name ______________________ Date ____________ LEARN **Grammar** 1

Sentences

- A **sentence** is a group of words that expresses a complete thought. Every sentence begins with a capital letter.
- A **sentence fragment** does not express a complete thought.
- A **declarative sentence** makes a statement. It ends with a period.
- An **interrogative sentence** asks a question. It ends with a question mark.

Read each sentence or phrase below. Write **S** beside it if it is a sentence. Write **F** if it is a fragment. Then add words to the fragments so that they express complete thoughts.

1. ______ Ed Sitrow is the captain of the losing soccer team.

____

2. ______ Proud of their losing season.

____

3. ______ The feeling of losing every game.

____

4. ______ Why does the team's attitude bother Ms. Appleton?

____

5. ______ Offers him a new bike in exchange for a win.

____

Put the correct mark of punctuation at the end of each sentence.

6. Why do the students hold a pep rally for the team

7. Radosh has a hard time understanding the importance of sports

8. What does Ed put on the team members' T-shirts

9. Ed asks Mr. Tillman if it isn't okay to lose

10. Mr. Lester never has coached soccer before

Extension: Give students a list of nouns, verbs, and adjectives (without drawing attention to the parts of speech). Challenge students to write three declarative sentences and three interrogative sentences using these words. Remind them to punctuate the sentences correctly.

Name ______________________ Date ____________

Types of Sentences

- An **imperative sentence** gives a command or makes a request. It ends with a period.

- An **exclamatory sentence** expresses strong feeling. It ends with an exclamation point.

Read each sentence. Write whether it is **declarative, interrogative, imperative,** or **exclamatory**.

1. What a great win that was! ______________________

2. Think about what Ed said about the rewards of losing. ______________________

3. How many games did the S.O.R. Losers play this season? ______________________

4. Don't laugh at Ed and his teammates. ______________________

5. Terry wondered about the team's attitude. ______________________

6. How clueless Coach Lester seems about soccer! ______________________

7. All of the teachers dislike the team's T-shirts. ______________________

8. Will the team win or lose its last game? ______________________

9. Please take pictures at the game. ______________________

10. Saltz writes poetry, and Lifsom paints pictures. ______________________

Extension: Have students work in pairs to conduct a brief interview with their partners about a subject or activity that is important to them. Then have the partners write up the questions and answers, punctuating each sentence correctly.

Writing Sentences

- A **sentence** is a group of words that expresses a complete thought.
- A **sentence fragment** does not express a complete thought.
- There are four types of sentences. A **declarative sentence** makes a statement and ends with a period. An **interrogative sentence** asks a question and ends with a question mark. An **imperative sentence** gives a command or makes a request. It ends with a period. An **exclamatory sentence** expresses strong feeling and ends with an exclamation point.

Identify the sentence type in the space provided. Then add the correct punctuation to each of the sentences.

______________ **1.** Talk to Ed about the team's chances for winning the game

______________ **2.** What an incredible mathematician Macht is

______________ **3.** Why are the Losers tired of people's words of encouragement

______________ **4.** Read the story to find out more about these seventh graders

______________ **5.** Have you ever felt the way these players do

______________ **6.** Parkville is the team that the Losers will play against next

______________ **7.** Please try to understand the teachers and the students

______________ **8.** How unusually the Losers talk and act

Extension: Have students choose five of the sentences above and rewrite them as different types of sentences. Then have them identify the types of sentences that they have written.

Sentence Punctuation

- Capitalize the first word of every sentence.
- End each sentence with the correct punctuation mark—a period, a question mark, or an exclamation mark.

The following paragraphs contain several errors. Rewrite the paragraphs so that every sentence begins with a capital letter and ends with the correct mark of punctuation.

do you want to know about the history of soccer? Soccer began as a school sport in England about 150 years ago It originally was called association football. In fact, the name "soccer" comes from the word "association" the game spread throughout Europe. from there it went to South America, the Middle East, and Asia countries from around the world were competing for soccer awards long before the game became popular in the United States How odd that seems now

americans' interest in soccer did not really grow until the 1970s. It was then that Brazilian soccer star Pelé became popular around the world have you heard of him He had the highest goal scoring rate in soccer history. because of Pelé, many Americans tried soccer and liked it

Today, soccer is the world's most popular sport. what an exciting game it can be The soccer championship, called the World Cup, is one of the most important prizes in sports the World Cup game was played in the United States for the first time in 1994

____

____

____

____

____

____

____

____

____

____

____

____

____

____

Extension: Ask students to write two of each of the four types of sentences without including any beginning capitalization or end punctuation. Have them exchange papers with classmates and add correct capitalization and end punctuation.

Name ______________________________ Date ____________ TEST **Grammar** 5

Sentences

Rewrite each group of words so that it is a sentence. The information in parentheses will tell you what type of sentence it should be. Be sure to begin each sentence with a capital letter and end it with the correct mark of punctuation.

1. each student at South Orange River Middle School (declarative)

____

2. avoid sports in the sixth grade (interrogative)

____

3. embarrassing to the school (exclamatory)

____

4. do not like so much attention (declarative)

____

5. to the newspaper reporter (imperative)

____

6. that pep rally (exclamatory)

____

7. with his teammates, Ed (declarative)

____

8. can't just let us lose (interrogative)

____

9. Mr. Tillman and Mr. Lester see your new T-shirts (imperative)

____

10. gave the team a few last pointers before the game (declarative)

____

/10

Sentences

- A **sentence** is a group of words that expresses a complete thought. There are four types of sentences: **declarative, interrogatory, imperative,** and **exclamatory**.

Mechanics:

- Capitalize the first word of every sentence.
- End each sentence with the correct punctuation mark—a period for declarative and imperative sentences, a question mark for interrogative sentences, or an exclamation point for exclamatory sentences.

Write four sentences that have something to do with playing or watching soccer. Make one sentence declarative, one interrogative, one imperative, and one exclamatory. When you are finished, read the sentences to a partner. Talk about how your voice helps identify the different types of sentences.

____

____

____

____

Subjects and Predicates

- The **complete subject** includes all the words that tell what or whom the sentence is about.
- The **simple subject** is the main word or words in the complete subject.
- You can sometimes correct a sentence fragment by adding a subject.

Read each sentence. Draw a line under the complete subject. Then circle the simple subject. (In some sentences, the complete subject and the simple subject may be the same.)

1. China was the Lins' original home.
2. Chinese people cool their soup by slurping it.
3. The narrator of this story remembers her embarrassment at their slurping.
4. The English language fascinates Mr. Lin.
5. Mrs. Lin memorizes lists of polite English phrases.
6. She does not always use the phrases correctly, however.
7. The Lins are surprised by the raw celery in the relish tray.
8. The Gleasons' other guests stare at the Lins' way of eating celery.
9. Meg Gleason talks to her friend about the party.
10. The Gleasons' dinner party was like a Chinese meal, after all.

Extension: Have groups of students write about an imaginary embarrassment. Challenge them to locate several complete subjects and simple subjects in their accounts.

Predicates

- The **complete predicate** includes all the words that tell what the subject does or is.
- The **simple predicate** is the main word in the complete predicate.
- You can sometimes correct a sentence fragment by adding a predicate.

Read each sentence. Draw a line under the complete predicate. Then circle the simple predicate. (In some sentences, the complete predicate and the simple predicate may be the same.)

1. Mr. Lin makes diagrams of verbs.
2. Meg and the narrator wear each other's clothes.
3. Without a pair of jeans, the narrator feels out of place.
4. Her mother buys her some jeans later.
5. The headwaiter of the Lakeview restaurant smiles.
6. Chow mein is an American dish, not a Chinese one.
7. Mr. Lin translates the menu with a French dictionary.
8. Four plates of soup arrive.
9. The Lins hold a dinner party for the Gleasons.
10. The Gleasons pile their plates high with food.

Extension: Ask students to write a short paragraph about visiting a restaurant. Have them look for complete predicates and simple predicates in their paragraphs.

Adding Subjects and Predicates

- The **complete subject** includes all the words that tell what or whom the sentence is about. The **simple subject** is the main word or words in the complete subject.
- The **complete predicate** includes all the words that tell what the subject does or is. The **simple predicate** is the main word in the complete predicate.
- You can sometimes correct a sentence fragment by adding a subject or predicate.

Rewrite these sentence fragments by adding subjects or predicates.

1. carry their chairs to the dining table

____

2. other students at school

____

3. Meg and the narrator

____

4. borrows a bike for a trip to the supermarket

____

5. fried Chinese dumplings

____

6. is a celebration of Mr. Lin's promotion

____

7. usually bring food from platters directly to their rice bowls

____

8. go out for a milkshake after dinner

____

Extension: Have the class list titles of favorite stories and films. Ask them to choose titles that they could turn into sentences, to add subjects or predicates as needed, and to share the results.

Letter Punctuation

- Begin the greeting and the closing of a letter with a capital letter.
- Use a comma after the greeting and closing in a friendly letter.
- Use a comma between the names of a city and a state.
- Use a comma between the day and year in a date.

Proofread this friendly letter for errors in commas and capitalization.

15 Pepperbush Lane

Madison CT 06447

April 23 2001

dear Gretchen

I had the best time at your house last week! You showed me so many wonderful things that I really got a good idea of what California living is like. The San Diego Zoo was my favorite. I also enjoyed the beach and our drive into Mexico. You are the best hostess, and I thank you for everything.

I look forward to seeing you on December 23 2001. That's when we both visit our grandparents. Toledo Ohio, may not be as exciting as San Diego, but I'm sure we'll have fun.

your friend

Meg

Extension: Have students write a friendly letter to a fictional or historical character. Urge them to observe the capitalization and comma conventions used in letters. Students might enjoy exchanging and proofreading their letters.

Name ______________________________ Date ____________

TEST
Grammar 11

Subjects and Predicates

Decide which group of words is the sentence part named in parentheses. Circle the letter of your answer.

1. Then Mrs. Gleason mixed together all the foods on her plate. (simple subject)
- **a.** mixed together all the foods on her plate
- **b.** mixed
- **c.** Mrs. Gleason
- **d.** Gleason

2. A frustrated Mr. Gleason picked up the pea with his fingers. (complete predicate)
- **a.** A frustrated Mr. Gleason
- **b.** picked up the pea with his fingers
- **c.** Mr. Gleason
- **d.** picked

3. The Chinese narrator gradually feels more at home. (simple predicate)
- **a.** feels
- **b.** gradually feels
- **c.** gradually feels more at home
- **d.** narrator gradually feels

4. A clever plan earns her a pair of jeans. (complete subject)
- **a.** a pair of jeans
- **b.** A clever plan
- **c.** earns her a pair of jeans
- **d.** plan

5. The narrator giggles at the Gleasons' way of eating Chinese food. (complete predicate)
- **a.** giggles
- **b.** the Gleasons' way of eating Chinese food
- **c.** The narrator
- **d.** giggles at the Gleasons' way of eating Chinese food

6. A platter of fruits is a fine Chinese dessert. (simple subject)
- **a.** A platter of fruits
- **b.** is a fine Chinese dessert
- **c.** platter
- **d.** fruits

7. Meg Gleason, the narrator's friend, wanted a chocolate milkshake. (complete subject)
- **a.** wanted a chocolate milkshake
- **b.** wanted
- **c.** Meg Gleason
- **d.** Meg Gleason, the narrator's friend

8. To the narrator's surprise, Meg makes slurping sounds with her drink. (simple predicate)
- **a.** Meg makes
- **b.** makes
- **c.** To the narrator's surprise, Meg
- **d.** makes slurping sounds with her drink

/8

Subjects and Predicates

- The **complete subject** includes all the words that tell what or whom the sentence is about. The **simple subject** is the main word or words in the complete subject.
- The **complete predicate** includes all the words that tell what the subject does or is. The **simple predicate** is the main word in the complete predicate.
- You can sometimes correct a sentence fragment by adding a subject or predicate.

Mechanics:

- Begin the greeting and the closing of a letter with a capital letter.
- Use a comma after the greeting and closing in a friendly letter.
- Use a comma between the names of a city and a state.
- Use a comma between the day and year in a date.

Proofread the letter Kathy wrote to her cousin Matt. Correct errors in capitalization, commas, and end punctuation.

410 birmingham Street
Kenosha WI 53140
May 1 2001

dear Matt

Remember when we went to the Chinese restaurant and neither of us could use chopsticks. Well, I finally learned how. It's easy! All it takes is a little practice.

hold both sticks in one hand, as if you were holding a pencil. The top chopstick should lie between your thumb and index finger. The bottom chopstick should lie between your middle and fourth fingers. Don't move that chopstick. It's the top chopstick that moves up and down to capture pieces of food. try it next time you go to a Chinese restaurant.

love
Kathy

Sentence Combining

- A **conjunction** joins words or groups of words. *And* adds information; *but* shows contrast; *or* gives a choice.
- A **compound sentence** contains two sentences joined by a comma and *and, but,* or *or.*
- You can form a compound sentence by joining two related sentences.

Put an X in front of each sentence that is a compound sentence. In those sentences, circle the word that joins the two shorter sentences.

1. ______ Lucinda was born in Cuba, but now she lives in the United States.

2. ______ Her brother makes friends easily, and soon he is on the school baseball team.

3. ______ Lucinda is lonely but won't admit it.

4. ______ Then Lucinda finds a homeless dog.

5. ______ Pieces of gum stick to Chauncey's belly, and hard candies are matted in his fur.

6. ______ The dog looks better after his bath, but there still is a problem.

7. ______ Pets are not allowed in the building, or Lucinda would keep Chauncey.

8. ______ Lucinda thinks about Ashley, a girl in her class.

9. ______ Ashley is friendly but not popular.

10. ______ Will Ashley take Chauncey, or must Lucinda find the dog another home?

Extension: Have students rewrite each compound sentence from this exercise as two simple sentences. For an extra challenge, have students rewrite the other sentences as two sentences, adding whatever words they feel are needed.

Compound Subjects and Compound Predicates

- A **compound subject** contains two or more simple subjects that have the same predicate.
- A **compound predicate** contains two or more simple predicates that have the same subject.
- You can combine two sentences by joining two subjects or two predicates with *and* or *or*.

Read the sentences. Draw one line under each compound subject. Draw two lines under each compound predicate. (Not every sentence has a compound subject or a compound predicate. One sentence has both.)

1. Lucinda's family left Cuba and settled in West New York.
2. Cars, trucks, and motorcycles make the town a noisy place.
3. Most houses have cement lawns and paved driveways.
4. Lucinda's parents work hard and return home late.
5. Lucinda's grandmother stayed in Cuba, but Lucinda thinks of her often.
6. Lucinda tried costumes and learned dances from her grandmother's friend.
7. A big front porch and bike rides to school are Lucinda's other memories of Cuba.
8. The girls at the new school dress in jeans, talk with boys, and giggle.
9. Most of the students come from Cuba or other parts of Latin America.
10. Lucinda and her brother go to the same school but have different lives there.

Extension: Have pairs of students collaborate on a short description of the town or city in which they live. Two sentences in the description should contain a compound subject; two should contain a compound predicate. Invite students to compare descriptions.

Combining Sentences

- A **compound sentence** contains two sentences joined with a comma and a conjunction.
- A **compound subject** contains two or more simple subjects that have the same predicate.
- A **compound predicate** contains two or more simple predicates that have the same subject.
- You can combine two related sentences by using a **conjunction**—*and, but,* or *or.* You can also combine two sentences by joining two subjects or two predicates with these conjunctions.

Read each set of sentences. Then combine them, using a conjunction to make one new sentence with a compound subject or a compound predicate.

1. The dog's paws were muddy. They looked swollen.

____

2. Lucinda rescued Chauncey. She had no place to keep him.

____

3. Her parents might be angry about this secret. The neighbors might be angry, instead.

____

Combine each set of sentences. Use a conjunction to make one compound sentence.

4. Lucinda must find Chauncey. He may go to the pound.

____

5. She looks everywhere with Ashley. The girls cannot find him.

____

6. Has there been a blackout? Is Chauncey still in the basement?

____

Extension: Have students look through a local newspaper for examples of compound sentences and sentences with compound subjects or compound predicates. In small groups, have them discuss the separate thoughts that were combined.

Name ______________________________ Date ____________ MECHANICS **Grammar** **16**

Punctuating Compound Sentences

- Use a comma before the conjunction in a compound sentence.
- If two parts of a compound sentence are not joined by a conjunction, use a semicolon to separate the parts.

Combine each set of sentences twice. The first time, use a comma and a conjunction in the compound sentence. The second time, use a semicolon.

1. Cuba is a foreign country. It is not far from the United States.

____

____

2. Havana is an important northern port. Guantánamo is an important southern port.

____

____

3. You might see parakeets in the trees. You might find a tortoise on the beach.

____

____

4. Many Cubans have Spanish ancestors. Other Cubans have African ancestors.

____

____

5. Spanish and African music were combined. Rumba music is one result.

____

____

6. Lucinda can dance to rumba music. She might learn that dance someday.

____

____

Extension: Call on a volunteer to suggest a simple sentence. Have another volunteer suggest a simple sentence related to it. Other volunteers can combine the sentences as they did for this worksheet; then continue with other sentences.

Combining Sentences

Revise the following paragraph to make it read more smoothly. Combine short sentences with a conjunction to form compound subjects, compound predicates, or compound sentences. Not every sentence needs to be combined or revised.

The largest island of the West Indies is Cuba. The largest nation of the West Indies is Cuba. The leader of Cuba, Fidel Castro, made life so hard for the people that many Cubans escaped to the United States. Most refugees wanted more political freedom. They hoped for better jobs. Most of the emigrants went to Florida. Some ended up in Europe. The voyage was dangerous and expensive. It was worth it. The refugees missed their families. They found freedom.

____

____

____

____

____

____

____

____

Name ______________________________ Date ____________

Combining Sentences

- You can combine two related sentences by using a conjunction. You can also combine two sentences by joining two subjects or two predicates with *and, or,* or *but*.

Mechanics

- Use a comma before the conjunction in a compound sentence. If two parts of a compound sentence are not joined by a conjunction, use a semicolon to separate the parts.

Rewrite the following sets of sentences. Create compound sentences or sentences with compound subjects or predicates. Use the correct punctuation. Then use the details from the sentences to draw a dog in the picture.

1. Scamp is a tall dog. He has thin legs.

____

2. Happy thoughts shine in his brown eyes. The thoughts make him a playful pet.

____

3. His tail curls over his back. It looks like a question mark.

____

4. Scamp's ears are white. His tail is white. He has large brown spots on his sides.

____

Complex Sentences and Clauses

- A **clause** is a group of words with a subject and a predicate.
- An **independent clause** can stand alone as a sentence
- A **dependent clause** cannot stand alone as a sentence.
- A dependent clause begins with a conjunction such as *wherever, before, while, because, as if,* or *unless.*

Read each group of words. Write **I** beside each independent clause. Write **D** beside each dependent clause. Then rewrite each dependent clause (taking away or adding words) so that it can stand alone as a sentence.

________ **1.** Whenever they see a dark cloud.

____

________ **2.** Because they are watching for showers.

____

________ **3.** George Wright does not share his wife's curiosity about the Sakkaros.

____

________ **4.** Although they are mysterious.

____

________ **5.** The Wrights are taking the Sakkaros to the park.

____

________ **6.** While the two boys enjoy the rides.

____

________ **7.** Mrs. Sakkaro holds her water glass in a napkin.

____

________ **8.** If they ate a warm hamburger?

____

Extension: Have students identify other subjects and predicates from "Rain, Rain, Go Away." Encourage them to experiment, using the subjects and predicates to form clauses. Discuss the results.

Name ______________________ Date ____________ LEARN AND PRACTICE **Grammar** 20

Complex Sentences

- A **complex sentence** contains an independent clause and one or more dependent clauses.
- When a dependent clause comes at the beginning of a sentence, use a comma after the dependent clause.
- When a dependent clause comes at the end, you usually do not use a comma.

Put an X in front of each complex sentence. If the dependent clause comes at the end of the sentence, rewrite the sentence so that the dependent clause comes at the beginning. If the dependent clause comes at the beginning of the sentence, rewrite so that it comes at the end. [Note: not every sentence is a complex one.]

________ 1. While she sunbathes, Mrs. Sakkaro keeps an eye on the sky.

____

________ 2. Tommie Wright has not yet made friends with the Sakkaros' son.

____

________ 3. The boy carries a barometer wherever he goes.

____

________ 4. Mrs. Wright will not be happy unless she can learn more about her neighbors.

____

________ 5. After she visits them, Mrs. Wright is even more curious.

____

________ 6. Before they agree to a trip, the Sakkaros check the weather forecast.

____

________ 7. Mr. Sakkaro plays his radio constantly, but no one can really hear it.

____

________ 8. As if someone has turned on a faucet, the rain suddenly falls.

____

Extension: Ask groups of students to write a letter that Mrs. Wright might have sent a friend after the events in this story. Have them include at least three complex sentences in their letters.

Name ______________________ Date ____________ PRACTICE AND REVIEW **Grammar** **21**

Writing Complex Sentences

- A **complex sentence** contains an independent clause and one or more dependent clauses.
- An **independent clause** can stand alone as a sentence.
- A **dependent clause** begins with a conjunction and cannot stand alone as a sentence.
- A **clause** is a group of words with a subject and a predicate.
- Use a comma after a dependent clause that comes at the beginning of a sentence, but usually do not use a comma if the dependent clause comes at the end.

Add either an independent or a dependent clause to each group of words to make complex sentences. Be sure to put commas in the correct places.

1. wherever they go

____

2. cotton candy is very sweet

____

3. if something warm or wet falls on them

____

4. they must go home immediately

____

5. the Sakkaros nervously ask George

____

6. as soon as they can arrange another outing

____

7. the rain begins

____

8. as though a giant dam has burst

____

Extension: Have students write four complex sentences about a storm. Then ask students to exchange papers and identify the independent and dependent clauses in the sentences that they receive.

Punctuating Complex Sentences

- When a dependent clause comes at the beginning of a sentence, use a comma after the dependent clause.
- When a dependent clause comes at the end of a sentence, you usually do not use a comma before the dependent clause.

Suppose that a reporter has come to interview the Wrights. Add commas to the dialogue where they are needed. Remove any commas that should not be there.

REPORTER: When the Sakkaros moved in did they seem odd to you?

MRS. WRIGHT: I feel sad, whenever I think of them. Although they were very strange, they didn't deserve—you know.

TOMMIE: Their son carried a barometer, wherever he went.

MRS. WRIGHT: Yes, and none of us knew, if Mr. Sakkaro had a job or not.

REPORTER: As you traveled to Murphy's Park did you suspect the tragedy to come?

MR. WRIGHT: No, everything seemed fine, while we drove there and enjoyed the rides.

MRS. WRIGHT: George is right. Until the sky got cloudy everything was fine.

TOMMIE: The Sakkaros were very nervous when they saw the clouds.

REPORTER: Because the rain fell what happened?

MR. WRIGHT: Unless I had seen it myself I would not have believed it. It was, as if a dam had burst and washed them away. As we watched, the Sakkaros melted!

REPORTER: What are your thoughts, since this all happened?

MRS. WRIGHT: I don't know, what I should think. After we lost the Sakkaros, though, I decided to be better to the neighbors we have left!

Complex Sentences

A. Each item gives part of a sentence; each possible answer gives another part. Try putting the parts together. Choose the answer that will result in a complex sentence. Circle the letter of your answer.

1. Mrs. Wright greeted the Sakkaros
  a. quickly.
  b. but has not seen them recently.
  c. when they moved in.

2. If the sky becomes cloudy,
  a. Mrs. Sakkaro makes her son come inside.
  b. and rain threatens.
  c. and dark.

3. George Wright works at home
  a. from time to time.
  b. but goes to the library for research.
  c. because he is a writer.

4. Unless they check the weather forecast,
  a. for the chance of rain.
  b. the Sakkaros are afraid to leave their house.
  c. and consult their fancy equipment.

B. Try making sentences from the different answers. Choose the answer that gives you a complex sentence with correct punctuation. Circle the letter of your answer.

5. Isaac Asimov came to the United States
  a. when he was three years old.
  b. , when he was three years old.
  c. , after being born in the Soviet Union.

6. Although he is best remembered for his stories
  a. , such as "Nightfall" and the Foundation novels.
  b. , and those stories have won many awards.
  c. , he wrote about science and other subjects.

Complex Sentences

- A **complex sentence** contains an independent clause and one or more dependent clauses.
- When a dependent clause comes at the beginning of a sentence, use a comma after the dependent clause.
- When a dependent clause comes at the end, you usually do not use a comma.

Study the picture and think about a science-fiction story that it might describe. Then read the following groups of words. Add ideas to turn the four groups of words into four complex sentences. Be sure to use commas correctly in the sentences.

1. wherever these space explorers travel

____

2. because she has spotted an interesting comet

____

3. everyone watches the approach of an alien ship

____

4. the captain hopes for a friendly first contact

____

Run-On Sentences

- A **run-on sentence** joins together two or more sentences that should be written separately.
- You can correct a run-on sentence by separating two complete ideas into two sentences.

Put an X in front of each sentence that is a run-on sentence.

________ **1.** A discovery in 1961 proved the Vikings' 1,000-year-ago visit to North America.

________ **2.** Before that time, the voyages of Leif Ericson were only a legend the legend was told in the *Icelandic Sagas*.

________ **3.** Newfoundland Island lies at the mouth of the Gulf of St. Lawrence it has a rocky, irregular coast and a flat interior.

________ **4.** Excavations there lasted several summers archeologists gradually uncovered the foundations of eight Viking buildings.

________ **5.** In 1964 one scientist found a tiny stone spinning wheel women had been among the 100 or so Vikings at the camp it had been their base of operations.

________ **6.** UNESCO—the United Nations Educational, Scientific, and Cultural Organization—named L'Anse aux Meadows a World Heritage Site.

________ **7.** W. Hodding Carter loved Viking culture as a boy, he had dreamed about Vikings one day, he had the chance to become a Viking.

________ **8.** Carter contacted Robert Stevens would Stevens build him a Viking ship?

________ **9.** Stevens was fascinated by the idea and agreed to Carter's plan.

________ **10.** A broken rudder ended their first voyage how eager they were to try again the next summer!

Extension: Have students choose four of the run-on sentences on this page and rewrite each one as separate sentences.

Name ______________________________ Date ____________ LEARN AND PRACTICE **Grammar** **26**

Run-on Sentences

- You can correct a run-on sentence by rewriting it as a compound or complex sentence.

Read these sentences. If a sentence is correct, write "**C.**" If it is a run-on sentence, rewrite it. Use separate sentences, compound sentences, and complex sentences in your revisions.

____ **1.** The Vikings were Scandinavian traders and settlers they spread throughout much of Europe and the North Atlantic.

____

____

____ **2.** Mapmakers once called the waters bordering Europe the Sea of Darkness sailors spoke of monsters and other dangers there.

____

____

____ **3.** Many sailors feared to venture out of sight of land the Vikings crossed vast bodies of water.

____

____

____ **4.** Viking sailors found their way by studying sea birds they also studied ocean currents.

____

____

____ **5.** These mariners were quite skillful they also figured out directions by observing the sun and stars.

____

____

____ **6.** A growing population, lack of farmland, and desire for wealth caused the Vikings to leave home.

____

Extension: Ask pairs of students to compare their revisions to the run-on sentences. For each sentence, urge them to try a method of revision that neither of them used previously. Discuss the results.

Correcting Run-On Sentences

- A **run-on sentence** joins together two or more sentences that should be written separately.
- You can correct run-on sentences in three different ways:
  1. Separate two complete ideas in a run-on sentence into two sentences.
  2. Rewrite the run-on sentence as a compound sentence.
  3. Rewrite the run-on sentence as a complex sentence.

Rewrite the following sentences to eliminate the run-on sentences. Try to use each of the three methods above at least once.

1. Ericson returned to Greenland one of his friends built the settlement in Vinland with a group of 150 people.

____

____

2. No one is sure why the Vikings left North America around 1013 sagas tell of fierce battles with the Eskimos.

____

____

3. The Portuguese came long after the Vikings they were also excellent sailors.

____

____

4. Prince Henry of Portugal realized that his country needed better ships and more able navigators navigators are people who plan and direct the course of a ship.

____

____

5. In 1419 he established a school for sailors he brought together astronomers, geographers, and mathematicians to share their learning.

____

____

Extension: Have students use one of the other two methods to revise each of the run-on sentences above.

Sentence Punctuation

- Capitalize the first word of every sentence and end with the correct punctuation mark.
- Use a comma before the conjunction in a compound sentence. If there is no conjunction, use a semicolon.
- Use a comma after a dependent clause at the beginning of a sentence.

Rewrite each sentence using proper capitalization, commas, and end punctuation.

1. Under the leadership of Erik the Red the first Viking expedition explored the southern coast of Greenland

____

____

2. In 986 a ship going to Greenland strayed too far south and its sailors discovered a new land.

____

____

3. scholars agree on the locations of two of Leif Ericson's landing places, Helluland (land of Flat Stones) and Markland (Wooded Land)

____

____

4. Helluland is the southeastern part of Baffin Island and Markland is on the coast of the Labrador Peninsula.

____

____

5. The location of Vinland has long been debated but most scholars agree that it was probably Newfoundland Island.

____

____

6. After uncovering the remains of a Viking settlement on Newfoundland experts believe that Vikings used the Vinland settlement for only a brief time.

____

____

Extension: Have students choose several passages from a magazine or newspaper and have them pick out the dependent and independent clauses and compound and complex sentences.

Run-On Sentences

Rewrite each run-on sentence, adding the punctuation and conjunctions shown in parentheses.

1. Maps are excellent records of exploration no one knows if the Vikings made maps. (Add a comma and the conjunction *but.*)

   ____

   ____

2. The oldest map of Vinland is the Skalholt map it dates from the mid-sixteenth century. (Add end punctuation and capitalization.)

   ____

   ____

3. It was made in 1570 by a schoolmaster he lived in the town of Skalholt, Iceland. (Add end punctuation and capitalization.)

   ____

   ____

4. The original map disappeared a copy from 1590 still exists. (Add a comma and the conjunction *but.*)

   ____

5. The map shows all the Viking sites it includes Helluland, Markland, and Vinland. (Add end punctuation and capitalization.)

   ____

6. The map is complete it is not very accurate. (Add a comma and the conjunction *but.*)

   ____

7. The map shows Greenland as a continent it is actually an island. (Add a comma and the conjunction *but.*)

   ____

8. A more accurate map exists it is believed by many to be a forgery. (Add punctuation and the conjunction *however.*)

   ____

Run-on Sentences

- A run-on sentence joins together two or more sentences that should be written separately.
- Correct a run-on sentence by using one of these methods:
  Separate two complete ideas into two sentences.
  Rewrite the run-on sentence as a compound sentence.
  Rewrite the run-on sentence as a complex sentence.

Mechanics:

- Capitalize the first word of every sentence and end with the correct punctuation mark.
- Use a comma before the conjunction in a compound sentence. If there is no conjunction, use a semicolon.
- Use a comma after a dependent clause at the beginning of a sentence.

Rewrite the run-on sentences using correct punctuation and capitalization.

1. The Egyptians built boats strong enough to sail on the Nile River they were too weak to withstand the force of the Mediterranean Sea.

____

____

2. The Egyptians discovered sailing their sails were usually square and made of cotton or papyrus.

____

____

3. Vikings believed the earth was flat they bravely sailed into the unknown.

____

____

4. On the open seas they watched for birds as a sign that land was near at night they steered by the North Star.

____

____

Name ______________________________ Date ____________

Sentences

Read the passage and look at each underlined section. Is there a mistake? If there is, how do you correct it? Circle the letter of your answer.

> Ed Sitrow wasn't ashamed of losing. In fact, he even promoted the idea that it was okay. Everyone loses sometimes. Yet, the S.O.R. soccer team lost all the time, and no one could understand it. The school had a winning tradition! (1) Everyone wanted Ed's team to win, too. They even held a pep rally to help the players. Go team! Go. (2) What do you think. (3) Is Ed right about losing?

1. **A.** Change *The* to *the.*
   B. Replace the exclamation point with a period.
   C. Replace the exclamation point with a question mark.
   D. No mistake.
2. **F.** Replace the period with an exclamation point.
   G. Change *Go* to *go.*
   H. Replace the period with a question mark.
   J. No mistake.
3. **A.** Change *What* to *what.*
   B. Replace the period with an exclamation point.
   C. Replace the period with a question mark.
   D. No mistake.

Read the passage below. How would you describe each group of underlined words? Circle the letter of your answer.

> It is difficult to know how to act when first living in a new culture. Every culture. (4) Has different manners and ways of doing things. The narrator's family. Learned many things about American culture. (5) They made mistakes. (6) There is no one way of eating or doing things, however. The narrator learned that by watching the Gleasons eat.

4. **A.** A complete sentence
   B. A sentence fragment missing a simple subject
   C. A sentence fragment missing a complete subject
   D. A sentence fragment missing a simple predicate
5. **F.** A complete sentence
   G. A sentence fragment missing a simple subject
   H. A sentence fragment missing a simple predicate
   J. A sentence fragment missing a complete predicate
6. **A.** A complete sentence
   B. A sentence fragment missing a simple subject
   C. A sentence fragment missing a complete subject
   D. A sentence fragment missing a simple predicate

Sentences

Read the passage. Circle the answer that describes each underlined sentence.

Lucinda finds a dog and takes him home. She can't keep him in her apartment, but she couldn't leave him to die. <u>Lucinda feeds and bathes Chauncey, and then she puts him in a small room.</u> **(7)** After she puts him in the room, the lights go out. He runs away, and she hurries out to find him. <u>Lucinda and Ashley go in search of Chauncey, but they do not find him.</u> **(8)**

7. **A.** Simple sentence with compound subject
   B. Simple sentence with compound predicate
   C. Compound sentence with compound subject
   D. Compound sentence with compound predicate

8. **F.** Simple sentence with compound subject
   G. Simple sentence with compound predicate
   H. Compound sentence with compound subject
   J. Compound sentence with compound predicate

Read the passage and look at each underlined sentence. Is there a mistake? If there is, how do you correct it? Circle the letter of your answer.

<u>While he was watching the ballgame George listened to Lillian.</u> **(9)** She had been watching their new neighbors. <u>She was curious about the Sakkaros because Mrs. Sakkaro always watched the sky.</u> **(10)** Lillian finally went over to meet them. Together, they planned an outing to Murphy's Park.

9. **A.** Add a comma after *ballgame*.
   B. Add a comma and a conjunction after *ballgame*.
   C. Add a conjunction after *ballgame*.
   D. No mistake.

10. **F.** Add a comma after *Sakkaros*.
    G. Add a comma and a conjunction after *Sakkaros*.
    H. Delete the conjunction *because* and add a comma.
    J. No mistake.

Common and Proper Nouns

- A **noun** names a person, place, thing, or idea.
- A **common noun** names any person, place, thing, or idea.
- A **proper noun** names a particular person, place, thing, or idea and begins with a capital letter.

Read each sentence. Then underline each common noun once and each proper noun twice.

1. Grandma looked tired and sad as she left the train.
2. The conductor announced Maizon's train in a loud voice, but Maizon really wasn't paying attention.
3. Margaret saw the tears in her eyes.
4. Margaret asks her mother about the difference between an old friend and a best friend.
5. Maizon goes away to boarding school in Connecticut.
6. Margaret reads her poem about her father and her best friend to Ms. Peazle and the sixth-grade class.
7. Margaret finds out that Hattie never liked Maizon because she didn't have common sense and she didn't tell the truth.
8. Margaret's mother is a talented artist who wants to be an architect.
9. Maizon must not have much time to write letters, or perhaps she has a new best friend.
10. Margaret is mourning both the death of her father and the departure of her best friend.

Extension: Have students identify as many common and proper nouns as they can locate in the classroom.

Proper Nouns

- Some proper nouns contain more than one word. Each important word begins with a capital letter.
- The name of a day, month, or holiday begins with a capital letter.

Identify all of the proper nouns in the following sentences. Rewrite each sentence, capitalizing the important words.

1. The M train crosses the williamsburg bridge into manhattan.

____

2. hattie is ms. Dell's daughter, and li'l jay is her son.

____

3. The group has to change trains at delancey street to get to penn station.

____

4. Even though the author, jacqueline woodson, does not tell us, maizon probably leaves for school around labor day in september.

____

____

5. The tory and dell families live somewhere between palmetto street and madison street.

____

Write a proper noun for each of the following categories.

6. building ____________________

7. day of the week ____________________

8. month ____________________

9. holiday ____________________

10. country ____________________

Extension: Have students add four or five more categories of proper nouns, such as people, states, book titles, product names, and geographic areas, and fill each category with at least two proper nouns.

Common and Proper Nouns

- A **common noun** names any person, place, thing, or idea.
- A **proper noun** names a particular person, place, thing, or idea, such as the names of days, months, or holidays.
- Proper nouns, which may consist of more than one word, are always capitalized.

Rewrite the following sentences, capitalizing all of the proper nouns.

1. maizon and her cousin jaime were in barcelona, spain, last fourth of july.

____

2. Daffodils, tulips, and hyacinths bloomed in march, just in time for easter Sunday.

____

3. Hattie's mother has an appointment with doctor weitzen next wednesday.

____

4. margaret's aunt pat was born in maine, but she moved to denver, colorado, because she fell in love with the rocky mountains.

____

____

5. ms. dell and her daughter hattie flew to mexico city for christmas.

____

Rewrite the sentences by changing each of the common nouns to proper nouns. You may have to change the wording of the sentence slightly. Be sure to capitalize proper nouns correctly.

6. The girl missed her friend.

____

7. The writer was born in the eastern part of the country.

____

8. My best friend liked this story.

____

9. Last month the family had a huge family picnic in the park in the city.

____

10. The girl planned to write to her friend.

____

Extension: Have students read a newspaper or magazine article and list all the proper nouns they find. Then have them categorize each noun as a person, place, thing, or idea.

Abbreviations

- An abbreviation is the shortened form of a word.
- Capitalize and put a period after abbreviations used in titles of respect (*Mrs., Ms., Mr., Dr., Rev.*).
- Capitalize and put a period after abbreviations for days, months, and addresses such as *St., Blvd., Ave.*

Insert capital letters and periods for the abbreviations in the following sentences.

1. Some people would rather not live on Lavender st, that winding road near the highway.

2. When ms Dell laughed, her assistant felt relieved.

3. The rev Joshua Felten will be attending the luncheon honoring mrs Andrews.

4. To receive a free copy of the pamphlet, send a self-addressed, stamped envelope to the Westside Women's Committee, 456 West Lake blvd, Los Angeles, CA 90024.

5. On thurs, sept 26, our class will be taking a field trip to the art museum, which is located at 1987 Field Club rd in Wilmington.

6. In feb my uncle, gen Michael Graves, will deliver the keynote address at the convention.

7. mr and mrs Stark moved from Blossom rd in Florida to Flower st in Georgia.

8. ms colletta's birthday, nov 9, falls on either a thurs or fri this year.

Extension: Have students find examples of abbreviations in newspaper articles. Direct them to make a list of these abbreviations and to include their spelled-out equivalents.

Common and Proper Nouns

Circle the letter of the correct form of capitalization for the underlined proper nouns. If the word or words is correctly capitalized, circle *c* for *no error.*

1. Margaret stayed at the Madison Hotel on boston post road.
   - a. boston post Road
   - b. Boston Post Road
   - c. no error
2. Hattie visited the colorado river.
   - a. Colorado River
   - b. Colorado river
   - c. no error
3. Margaret wants to see all of the continents of australia and north america.
   - a. Australia and north America
   - b. Australia and North America
   - c. no error
4. Before Independence Day we will celebrate Memorial Day.
   - a. independence day, memorial day
   - b. Independence day, Memorial day
   - c. no error
5. Hattie dated her letter may 9, addressed it to mr. Mullens, and put on enough extra postage to send her response to london, England.
   - a. May, Mr., London
   - b. may, mr., London
   - c. no error
6. Margaret reads the *national geographic* magazine in doctor Wong's office.
   - a. *National Geographic*, Doctor
   - b. *National Geographic*, doctor
   - c. no error
7. Margaret gazed at the declaration of independence.
   - a. Declaration Of Independence
   - b. Declaration of Independence
   - c. no error
8. On Mother's Day, Hattie gave her mother Iris soap.
   - a. Mother's day, iris
   - b. Mother's Day, iris
   - c. no error

Common and Proper Nouns

- A common noun names any person, place, thing, or idea.
- A proper noun names a particular person, place, thing, or idea.
- Some proper nouns may contain more than one word. Capitalize each important word.

Mechanics:

- An abbreviation is the shortened form of a word.
- Capitalize and put a period after abbreviations used in titles of respect (*Mrs., Ms., Mr., Dr., Rev.*)
- Capitalize and put a period after abbreviations for days, months, and addresses such as *St., Blvd., Ave.*

Read the following nouns. Decide whether each noun should be written with a capital letter. Then write each noun under the correct picture.

1. christianity
2. river playhouse
3. olympic games
4. perfume
5. chatham college
6. dinner ______________ ______________
7. maizon ______________ ______________
8. bus driver ______________ ______________
9. democracy ______________ ______________
10. friendship ______________ ______________

Name ______________________ Date ____________

Singular and Plural Nouns

- A **singular noun** names one person, place, thing, or idea.
- A **plural noun** names more than one person, place, thing, or idea.
- Add *-s* to form the plural of most singular nouns.

Read each sentence. Underline each singular noun, and circle each plural noun.

1. Mary Whitebird has nightmares about an endurance ritual celebrated by some Native Americans.
2. Some families on her reservation are beginning to give up the old customs in favor of more modern ideas.
3. Mary and Roger try to argue about the custom, but their protests are ignored.
4. Mary's teacher points out that girls have the opportunity to compete on equal terms with boys.
5. Mary and Roger are expected to survive in the woods for five days by eating insects, roots, and berries.

Write the plural form of each singular noun below.

6. shoe ______________
7. braid ______________
8. tribe ______________
9. originator ______________
10. council ______________
11. warrior ______________
12. area ______________
13. time ______________
14. hundred ______________
15. omelet ______________
16. legend ______________
17. circumstance ______________
18. cent ______________
19. morning ______________
20. experience ______________

/20

Extension: Have students list ten singular nouns and ten plural nouns that they associate with growing up or growing older.

Singular and Plural Nouns

- Add *-es* to form the plural of singular nouns that end in *s, sh, ch,* or *x*.
- To form the plural of nouns ending in a consonant and *y*, change *y* to *i* and add *-es*.
- To form the plural of nouns ending in a vowel and *y,* add *-s*.

Correct the misspellings of the plural nouns in these sentences.

1. Mary has fantasys about knights in shining armor and beautiful ladys in long gowns.

____

2. In her grandfather's day, boys and girls had to watch out for enemys who might try to capture them. ______________________

3. Roger and Mary plan to stake out their territorys and find a stash of berrys.

____

4. They were not worried about foxs or other wild animals hiding behind bushs.

____

5. Mary's wishs were ignored, but she expected no crutchs or special delayes.

____

Write the plural form of each singular noun below.

6. wax ______________

7. factory ______________

8. flash ______________

9. journey ______________

10. donkey ______________

11. speech ______________

12. community ______________

13. mass ______________

14. box ______________

15. army ______________

16. dish ______________

17. lily ______________

18. monkey ______________

19. glass ______________

20. mix ______________

Extension: Have students choose five of the nouns above and write two sentences for each, one using the singular form and the other the plural form.

Singular and Plural Nouns

- Add *-s* to form the plural of most singular nouns.
- Add *-es* to form the plural of singular nouns that end in *s, sh, ch, or x*.
- To form the plural of nouns ending in a consonant and *y*, change *y* to *i* and add *-es*.
- To form the plural of nouns ending in a vowel and *y*, add *-s*.

One plural form in each numbered line is misspelled. Write the misspelled word correctly.

__________	**1.**	friends	boxs	coaches
__________	**2.**	comedies	licenses	eyelashs
__________	**3.**	churchs	boys	taxis
__________	**4.**	sandwiches	attornies	kisses
__________	**5.**	birches	cherries	babys

One noun in each sentence should be made plural. Find that one noun and write the sentence correctly.

6. Roger's and Mary's Ta-Na-E-Ka rituals are like a voyage of discovery.

____

7. Roger gathers different moss to sit on because he does not like the hardness of bare ground.

____

8. Mary looks at the arch of the many trees and feels as if the woods are closing in on her.

____

9. Both children know several approach to the nearby town.

____

10. They spend time gathering large quantity of food.

____

/10

Extension: Have students write a short paragraph about a familiar rite of passage, such as learning to ride a bike. Tell them to use as many singular nouns as they can. Then ask students to exchange papers with a classmate and rewrite the paragraph, changing singular nouns to plural nouns wherever it makes sense to do so.

Commas in a Series

- A comma tells the reader to pause between the words that it separates.
- Use commas to separate three or more words in a series.
- Do not use a comma after the last word in a series.

Rewrite each sentence, inserting commas in the correct places.

1. Mary gathered berries roots and fruit.

____

2. The Navajo Hopi and Zuni are Native Americans of the southwest.

____

3. Survival in the wilderness requires knowledge courage and endurance.

____

4. Native American traditions are ancient meaningful and sacred.

____

5. The Navajo religion places great value on harmony balance and healing.

____

6. Native Americans lived in tepees lodges and longhouses.

____

7. Native Americans adapted to the conditions of the woodlands the deserts and the frozen north.

____

____

8. Peoples of the woodland areas lived on fish game and vegetation.

____

9. Native Americans of the desert learned how to cultivate food conserve water and protect themselves from heat of the sun.

____

____

10. Native peoples of the far north found uses for the flesh bone and skins of whales.

____

Extension: Have students write five sentences that contain items in a series, but tell them not to insert commas. Direct them to exchange papers with a classmate and punctuate each other's sentences.

Name ______________________ Date ____________ TEST **Grammar** 43

Singular and Plural Nouns

Complete the following sentences. Use the plural form of the noun in parentheses.

1. Mary wanted her ____________ on time. (meal)

2. The ____________ were running across the field. (fox)

3. The ____________ of the tree were in the way. (branch)

4. The ____________ were thick and green. (leaf)

5. Fog was thick over the ____________. (marsh)

6. The deer ate all the tender ____________ of grass. (blade)

7. The Native Americans' ____________ were swift and hardy. (pony)

8. The ____________ of the birds warned the deer that someone was coming. (screech)

9. The mice hid in the thick ____________. (bush)

10. The ____________ hopped across the big pond. (frog)

11. ____________ of sunlight shone through the trees. (flash)

12. Roger picked some ____________ to eat for breakfast. (berry)

13. ____________ of wild grapes grew on the vine. (bunch)

14. He buried the ____________ of the campfire. (ash)

/14

Nouns

- A plural noun names more than one person, place, thing, or idea
- Add *-s* to form the plural of most singular nouns.
- Add *-es* to form the plural of singular nouns that end in *s, sh, ch,* or *x*.
- To form the plural of nouns ending in a consonant and *y*, change *y* to *i* and add *-es*.
- To form the plural of nouns ending in a vowel and y, add *-s*.

Mechanics:

- Use commas to separate three or more words in a series.
- Do not use a comma after the last word in a series.

Work with a partner. One partner reads a sentence, changing the singular nouns to plural nouns. The other partner writes the sentence correctly, using commas where they are needed. Exchange papers to proofread each other's sentences.

1. In different part of the world, teenager must cut their tie to their childhood.

____

2. They are expected to act like mature adult accept responsibility and play important role in the community.

____

____

3. Elaborate ceremony get them ready to become adult.

____

4. Some Native American spend time alone outdoor on a vision quest, during which they receive guidance from nature ancestor or spirit animal.

____

____

5. In Papua, New Guinea, people believe that childhood bond are so strong that they must be cut.

____

____

6. Boy must prove they are strong brave and stubborn enough to withstand pain.

____

Name ______________________ Date ____________ LEARN **Grammar** 45

More Plural Nouns

- To form the plural of most nouns ending in *f* or *fe*, add *-s*.
- For others, change the *f* to *v* and add *-es*.

Write the plural form of each singular noun below.

1. shelf ____________

2. puff ____________

3. loaf ____________

4. knife ____________

5. spoof ____________

6. chef ____________

7. dwarf ____________

8. wolf ____________

Rewrite these sentences using the correct plural form.

9. During World War II, many wife took their husbands' place at work

____

10. Many Jewish people in Europe lost their life during World War II.

____

11. Bombs fell on roof and destroyed homes.

____

12. After the war, Germany was divided into two halfs.

____

Extension: To help students begin to memorize these plural noun forms, organize a spelling bee.

Name ______________________ Date ______________ LEARN AND PRACTICE **Grammar** 46

More Plural Nouns

- To form the plural of nouns that end with a vowel and *o*, add *-s*.
- To form the plural of nouns that end with a consonant and *o*, add *-s* or *-es*.
- Some nouns have special plural forms.
- A few nouns have the same singular and plural forms.

Write the plural form of each singular noun below.

1. goose ______________

2. rodeo ______________

3. headquarters ______________

4. potato ______________

5. ox ______________

6. ratio ______________

7. silo ______________

8. mouse ______________

9. concerto ______________

10. wolf ______________

Extension: Have students write a brief paragraph in which they use five of the words above in plural form.

More Plural Nouns

- To form the plural of most nouns ending in *f* or *fe,* add *-s.*
- For other nouns, change the *f* to *v* and add *-es.*
- To form the plural of nouns that end with a vowel and *o,* add *-s.*
- To form the plural of nouns that end with a consonant and *o,* add *-s* or *-es.*
- Some nouns have special plural forms that must be memorized.
- A few nouns have the same singular and plural forms.

Read each sentence. If the sentence contains an incorrect plural form, rewrite it using the correct plural form. If the sentence is correct, write *C* on the line.

1. Papa tore the photoes from the album. ____________

2. The soldiers carried knifes. ____________

3. The children hid in the bedroom. ____________

4. Some hungry familys had little to eat during the war. ____________

5. A few potatos would seem like a feast to the starving children.

____

6. The Danes listened to their radioes. ____________

7. Many Danes became heros during the German occupation.

____

8. The Rosens had salmon for dinner. ____________

9. The presence of the soldiers increased the worrys of the people.

____

10. The soldiers stole loafs of bread from the people. ____________

11. The mans watched the fleet being destroyed. ____________

12. Womans helped in the war effort. ____________

13. The childs were in great danger. ____________

14. Many Danish people saved their Jewish friends. ____________

15. People hoped the Allies would land on the beachs. ____________

Extension: To help students practice the formation of plural nouns, have them make flash cards with the singular spelling on the front and the plural spelling on the back. Give pairs of students time to quiz each other.

Capitalization and Abbreviations

- Capitalize names of people, places, organizations, and languages.
- Capitalize names of family members that refer to specific people.
- Capitalize and put a period after abbreviations of days, months, addresses, and titles of respect.

Proofread these sentences. Write them correctly on the lines.

1. kirsti, annemarie, and ellen want to go to tivoli in copenhagen, denmark, to see the fireworks.

   ____

2. Ellen Rosen's Mother and Father hid from the germans.

   ____

3. Adolf Hitler directed his armies from berlin, Germany.

   ____

4. Gen Dwight D. Eisenhower led the Allied forces.

   ____

5. Pres Roosevelt was commander-in-chief of the United States military forces.

   ____

6. The president of the united states lives at 1600 pennsylvania avenue, washington, D.C.

   ____

7. Prime Minister Winston Churchill was in london, england, during the war.

   ____

8. In the newspaper article, the reporter mistakenly gave sgt harvey munroe's address as 389 s. tiburon ave.

   ____

   ____

9. According to the history books, december 7, 1941, marked the entry of the United States into the war.

   ____

   ____

10. On may 8, 1945, Americans celebrated their victory over the Axis forces in europe.

   ____

Extension: Have students write a business letter to a travel agent requesting information about a place that interests them. Tell them to use correct capitalization and abbreviations.

Name ______________________ Date ____________ TEST **Grammar** 49

More Plural Nouns

Circle the noun or nouns that are spelled correctly in each row.

1. bluffs	wifes	species
2. siloes	believes	zoos
3. oxes	volcanoes	bailiffs
4. lives	studioes	crises
5. waifs	tariffs	trouser
6. safes	radioes	deers
7. banjoes	moose	womans
8. mouses	wolves	videos

Rewrite the nouns above that are not spelled correctly.

9. ______________________

10. ______________________

11. ______________________

12. ______________________

13. ______________________

14. ______________________

15. ______________________

16. ______________________

More Plural Nouns

- To form the plural of most nouns ending in *f* or *fe,* add *-s*.
- For other nouns, change the *f* to *v* and add *-es*.
- To form the plural of nouns that end with a vowel and *o*, add *-s*.
- To form the plural of nouns that end with a consonant and *o*, add *-s* or *-es*.
- Some nouns have special plural forms that must be memorized.
- A few nouns have the same singular and plural forms.

Mechanics:

- Capitalize names of people, places, organizations, and languages.
- Capitalize names of family members that refer to specific people.
- Capitalize and put a period after abbreviations of days, months, addresses, and titles of respect.

Correct the errors in plural nouns in each sentence. Write the sentence with the correct capital letters. Above, draw the picture that the sentences describe.

1. The chieves of the Allied armies met in a tent.

____

2. They listened on their radioes for news from their troops.

____

3. Troops waited at the wharfs for supplies and mail from home.

____

4. Mail came from friends and wifes in the united states.

____

Possessive Nouns

- A possessive noun is a noun that shows who or what owns or has something.
- Form a singular possessive noun by adding an apostrophe (') and *-s* to a singular noun.

Circle the possessive noun or nouns in each sentence. Then write what the possessive noun owns or has.

1. Huynh's job is to look after the family's herd of water buffalo. ______________
2. The boy's first trip to the jungle takes place when he is twelve. ______________
3. Grandmother's teeth are so strong that she can eat corn on the cob. ______________
4. His mother's logic is not understood by anyone but his grandmother. ______________
5. His grandmother cannot tolerate the rascal's behavior. ______________
6. The rascal is really the world's biggest chicken. ______________
7. Vietnam's beauty is well known. ______________
8. The average farmer's rice yield is much larger this year than last. ______________
9. The country's economy is still struggling. ______________
10. Opera's standard characters include the Villain, the Faithful One, and the Flatterer. ______________

Extension: Have students shorten groups of words like the following by using singular possessive nouns: the cover of the book, the tusks of the elephant, the slyness of the fox.

Forming Plural Possessive Nouns

- A plural possessive noun is a plural noun that shows ownership.
- To form the possessive of a plural noun that ends in *-s*, add an apostrophe.
- To form the possessive of a plural noun that does not end in *-s*, add an apostrophe and *-s*.

Write the plural possessive form for each of the singular possessive nouns below.

1. farmer's ______________
2. student's ______________
3. child's ______________
4. boss's ______________
5. nurse's ______________
6. garden's ______________
7. tree's ______________
8. moose's ______________
9. brush's ______________
10. story's ______________
11. villager's ______________
12. buffalo's ______________
13. bandit's ______________
14. captain's ______________
15. husband's ______________
16. writer's ______________
17. thief's ______________
18. man's ______________
19. daughter's ______________
20. century's ______________

Extension: Have students choose 5 of the nouns listed above and write sentences for both the singular possessive and plural possessive forms.

Name ______________________ Date ____________ LEARN **Grammar** 57

Appositives

- An **appositive** is a word or group of words that follows a noun and identifies or explains the noun.
- Commas are used to set off most appositives from the rest of the sentence.

Read each sentence. If the sentence contains an appositive, write **A** on the line and underline the appositive word or phrase. If the sentence does not contain an appositive, write **N**.

1. Cleopatra's palace was on an island near Alexandria, the capital city of Egypt. ____

2. Alexandria was named after Alexander the Great. ____

3. Franck Goddio, an undersea explorer, found the palace. ____

4. Pillars, statues, and parts of the cobblestone streets are the only remains of the city. ____

5. The divers uncovered two statues of sphinxes, creatures with the head of a human and the body of a lion. ____

6. Cleopatra, the last Pharaoh of Egypt, collected beautiful art and sculpture. ____

7. The Egyptians worshipped Ra, the sun god. ____

8. The romance between Mark Antony and Cleopatra was not popular among Roman leaders. ____

9. Cleopatra once was in love with Julius Caesar, the Roman general, statesman, and dictator. ____

10. Did you know that Julius Caesar made Cleopatra a queen? ____

Extension: Have students look through a newspaper or magazine, locate three appositives or appositive phrases, and share them with the class.

Appositives

- You can use an appositive to combine two short sentences into one.

Read each pair of sentences. Then combine them using an appositive word or phrase. Be sure to write the new sentence using a comma or commas to set off the appositive.

1. Alexander the Great was a skillful military leader. He was the king of Macedonia.

____

2. He was born in Pella. Pella was the Macedonian capital.

____

3. Young Alexander studied with Aristotle. Arisototle was one of the most famous philosophers of that time.

____

____

4. Alexander became king when Philip was murdered in 336 B.C. Philip was his father.

____

5. Alexander invaded Persia two years later. Persia was a neighbor to the southeast.

____

6. He conquered the Persians and then moved upon Egypt. Egypt was his next target.

____

Extension: Ask students to use appositives to write five sentences about a real or fictional treasure. Have them exchange papers with a partner and identify the appositives in the sentences they receive.

Appositives

- An **appositive** is a word or group of words that follows a noun and identifies or explains the noun.
- Commas are used to set off most appositives from the rest of the sentence.
- You can use an appositive to combine two short sentences into one.

Use appositives to combine each pair of sentences. Be sure to place the commas correctly.

1. Alexander the Great carefully planned Alexandria. It was the city that he named after himself.

____

____

2. On Pharos, he had an amazing lighthouse built. Pharos was an island in the harbor.

____

____

3. It became one of the Seven Wonders of the Ancient World. It was a sight beyond compare.

____

____

4. Poseidon was recognized with a beautiful temple in Alexandria. Poseidon was the Greek god of the sea.

____

____

5. One special place helped make the city a famous center of learning. That place was the Alexandrian Library and Museum.

____

____

6. After Cleopatra's death, control of Alexandria went to Octavian. Octavian was a Roman who later became Caesar Augustus.

____

____

Extension: Have pairs of students gather information about a city that interests them. Ask them to collaborate on a brief oral report on that place, using at least three appositives in their presentation.

Commas with Appositives

- Use commas to set off most appositives from the rest of the sentence.

Add commas where they are needed to set off appositives in the following sentences.

1. How I would like to be an emperor a ruler over a powerful nation!

2. My palace a large building on a high hill would be fabulous.

3. The main entrance would be surrounded by statues images of smart and good people.

4. My throne room the highest room in the palace would have a view of the capital city.

5. I also would have a television studio a place where I could broadcast to the people.

6. Of course, the video arcade my favorite place to relax would be amazing.

7. How quickly could my chef a skillful cook prepare my favorite foods?

8. There also would be several places that my subjects the people could use.

9. My library a separate building on the palace grounds would have every book a sixth grader might need.

10. Sometimes I the emperor might even work as a library assistant there.

Extension: Have students write five sentences that contain appositives but no commas. Have them exchange papers with a partner and insert commas where needed.

Name ______________________ Date ____________

TEST
Grammar 61

Appositives

A. Rewrite the following sentences. Underline the appositive word or phrase, adding commas where they are needed.

1. Egypt the home of an ancient civilization is an interesting place.

____

2. On the east, it is separated from Israel by the Red Sea an inland sea.

____

3. Sudan and Libya two other African nations share borders with Egypt.

____

4. The Qattara Depression the lowest spot in Africa is in Egypt.

____

B. Use appositives to combine each pair of sentences. Be sure to place the commas correctly.

5. Southern Egypt is the home of the Nubian Desert. That desert is a hot and sandy place.

____

6. There you can also find Lake Nasser. It is a huge reservoir.

____

7. The Sinai Peninsula lies to the northeast. The Sinai Peninsula is a place mentioned in the Bible.

____

____

8. Egypt is an African country, but the Sinai Peninsula is considered part of Asia. The Sinai Peninsula is a part of Egypt.

____

____

Appositives

- An **appositive** is a word or group of words that follows a noun and identifies or explains the noun. You can use an appositive to combine two short sentences into one.

Mechanics:

- Use commas to set off most appositives from the rest of the sentence.

In the space above, draw a picture of a palace. Then write four sentences about it, using these groups of words as appositives. (You may make up some "make-believe" nouns, if you wish.) Be sure to place commas correctly.

1. a place of rare beauty

____

____

2. a building 1,000 feet tall

____

____

3. the home of their king and queen

____

____

4. a river that flows nearby

____

____

Name ________________________________ Date ____________ REVIEW **Grammar** 63

Nouns

Read the passage and look at each underlined section. Is there a mistake? If there is, how do you correct it? Circle the letter of your answer.

<u>When Margaret's Father died, it marked the beginning of a tragic summer in New York City</u> **(1)**. She also lost her best friend. <u>School started in september, and it seemed life was even worse</u> **(2)**. <u>When her teacher, Ms. Peazle, asked her to write about her feelings, Margaret wrote a poem</u> **(3)**. It helped her understand her feelings.

1. **A.** Change *New York City* to *New York city.*
   B. Capitalize *summer.*
   C. Change *Father* to *father.*
   D. No mistake.

2. **F.** Capitalize *september.*
   G. Capitalize *life.*
   H. Capitalize *it.*
   J. No mistake.

3. **A.** Capitalize *teacher.*
   B. Change *Ms.* to *ms.*
   C. Capitalize *poem.*
   D. No mistake.

<u>Some familys didn't make girls go on Ta-Na-E-Ka. Mary Whitebird had to go, and she tested her endurance in unexpected ways</u> **(4)**. <u>She didn't sleep under bushes or eat grasshoppers and butterflies. She slept in a restaurant and her lunchs consisted of hamburgers and milk shakes</u> **(5)**. When she returned from her Ta-Na-E-Ka, she told what she had done and how she had survived.

4. **A.** Change *familys* to *families.*
   B. Change *girls* to *girles.*
   C. Change *ways* to *wayes.*
   D. No mistake.

5. **F.** Change *bushes* to *bushs.*
   G. Change *grasshoppers* to *grasshopperes.*
   H. Change *butterflies* to *butterflys.*
   J. Change *lunchs* to *lunches.*

Nouns

The night the Nazis marched in like wolves must have been terrifying. Earlier in the evening, perhaps the children had played with their dolls. **(6)** The characters in *Gone with the Wind* were their heros. Now, as it gets dark, Annemarie and Ellen stare out over the roofs of the town. The leafs on the trees rustle in the wind. **(7)** Were their lives about to change? Father pulls nervously on the cuffs of his shirtsleeves. His beliefs are about to be tested. **(8)**

6. **A.** Change *wolves* to *wolfs.*
   B. Change *heros* to *heroes.*
   C. Change *children* to *childrens.*
   D. No mistake.

7. **F.** Change *roofs* to *rooves.*
   G. Change *leafs* to *leaves.*
   H. Change *lives* to *lifes.*
   J. No mistake.

8. **A.** Change *beliefs* to *believes.*
   B. Change *cuffs* to *cuves.*
   C. Change *shirtsleeves* to *shirtsleeveses.*
   D. No mistake.

Huynh Quang Nhuong tells about his grandparents lives in Vietnam. The author's village was in the central highlands. **(9)** The villagers lived by farming and hunting. Every farmer's children had to work from a young age. The childrens' jobs were in the house and fields. **(10)**

9. **A.** Change *grandparents* to *grandparents's.*
   B. Change *grandparents* to *grandparents'.*
   C. Change *author's* to *authors'.*
   D. Change *author's* to *authors.*

10. **F.** Change *farmer's* to *farmers's.*
    G. Change *farmer's* to *farmers.*
    H. Change *childrens'* to *children's.*
    J. Change *childrens'* to *childrens's.*

Name ______________________________ Date ____________

Action Verbs

- An action verb is a word that expresses action. It tells what the subject does or did.
- A direct object is a noun or pronoun that receives the action of the verb. It answers the question *what?* or *whom?* after the verb.

Underline the action verbs and circle the direct objects in the following sentences.

1. Calvin Stanley likes color.

2. Calvin learns many skills.

3. His mother showed him the sharp edges of the table.

4. Calvin uses his hands instead of his eyes.

5. One of his cousins got a new bike.

6. Mr. Stanley taught Calvin.

7. Calvin rides his bike in the alley behind his house.

8. Calvin's mother covers her eyes with her hands.

9. Calvin even plays the piano.

10. He watches wrestling on television every Saturday.

11. He likes his teachers.

12. Calvin reads Braille very quickly.

Extension: Have students work in pairs to identify action verbs and direct objects in a magazine or newspaper article.

Indirect Objects

- An indirect object is a noun or pronoun in the predicate that answers the question *to whom*? or *for whom*? or *to what*? or *for what*? after an action verb.

Underline each action verb once and each direct object twice. Circle each indirect object.

1. Mrs. Sivits gave Calvin some lessons.

2. Experience has taught Calvin many things.

3. The teacher read the class a story.

4. Brian gives his best friend good advice.

5. Mrs. Sivits teaches her students Braille.

6. Louis Braille gave blind people a way to read.

7. Helen Keller wrote the President a letter.

8. Anne Sullivan taught Helen Keller many skills.

9. Many organizations offered Helen Keller awards.

10. Schools give blind students excellent opportunities.

11. Calvin played his mother music.

12. Stevie Wonder sings us his songs.

Extension: Ask students to write a paragraph about someone they know who has an unusual talent. Direct them to underline each action verb once and each direct object twice. Tell them to circle each indirect object.

Action Verbs and Objects

- An action verb is a word that expresses action. It tells what the subject does or did.
- A direct object is a noun or pronoun that receives the action of the verb. It answers the question what? or whom? after the verb.
- An indirect object is a noun or pronoun in the predicate that answers the question to whom? or for whom? or to what? or for what? after an action verb. An indirect object always comes before a direct object.

Read each sentence. Then in the three columns below, write the word from each sentence that fits under the column heading.

1. Calvin shows us his room.

2. Mrs. Stanley read her son the story.

3. Calvin handed Kellie her bike.

4. Mrs. Stanley threw him the ball.

5. Monet gave Calvin the signal.

6. Mr. Stanley brought his son some toys.

7. Calvin asked his teacher a question.

8. Calvin offers Miss Dyer his hand.

	Action Verbs	Indirect Objects	Direct Objects
1.	________	________	________
2.	________	________	________
3.	________	________	________
4.	________	________	________
5.	________	________	________
6.	________	________	________
7.	________	________	________
8.	________	________	________

Extension: Give students brief sentences with direct objects and have them add indirect objects.
Sample sentence: Renee will lend her copy.
Student response: Renee will lend Sonja her copy.

Name ______________________ Date ____________

Commas in a Series

- Use commas to separate three or more words in a series.
- Do not use a comma after the last word in a series.

Insert commas in the following sentences where they are needed.

1. Calvin Stanley is curious self-confident and imaginative.

2. He rides a bike plays baseball and puts toys together.

3. His mother is a smiling handsome strong-looking woman.

4. Some of Calvin's toys include records tapes and a talking robot.

5. Teachers vision specialists and mobility instructors have helped Calvin adjust.

6. A girl in Calvin's class has red yellow and blue barrettes in her hair.

7. Braille is used for mathematics science and written language.

8. Miss Dyer Mrs. Jackson and Miss Sivits are Calvin's teachers.

9. Calvin likes to play baseball with Kellie Monet and his mother.

10. Calvin's father taught him how to ride a bike to shift gears and to play many different games.

Extension: Have students write a letter to a friend or family member about a real or imagined trip to a favorite place. Tell them to use at least four series of nouns, verbs, adjectives, or adverbs in their letter and to punctuate each series correctly with commas.

Name ______________________________ Date ____________ TEST **Grammar** 69

Action Verbs and Objects

Read each sentence. Write whether the underlined word is a direct object, an indirect object, or an action verb.

1. Calvin <u>rides</u> his bike in the alley.

    ____

2. Mrs. Jackson asks her students a <u>question</u>.

    ____

3. Calvin <u>told</u> Brian a joke.

    ____

4. Mr. Stanley brought his <u>son</u> a toy truck.

    ____

5. Mrs. Stanley played <u>Calvin</u> a record.

    ____

6. Calvin <u>told</u> Brian about the story.

    ____

7. The teacher gave the class <u>homework</u>.

    ____

8. He read the Braille <u>book</u> out loud.

    ____

9. Kellie and Brian <u>told</u> Calvin about the movie.

    ____

10. Calvin told his <u>teacher</u> the answer.

    ____

Action Verbs and Objects

- An action verb is a word that expresses action. It tells what the subject does or did.
- A direct object is a noun or pronoun that receives the action of the verb. It answers the question *what?* or *whom?* after the verb.
- An indirect object is a noun or pronoun in the predicate that answers the question *to whom?* or *for whom?* or *to what?* or *for what?* after an action verb. An indirect object always comes before a direct object.

Mechanics:

- Use commas to separate three or more words in a series.
- Do not use a comma after the last word in a series.

Look at the picture. Rewrite each sentence, using the picture to help describe it. Add the sentence part or punctuation shown in parentheses.

1. The teacher gave a book. (Add an indirect object.)

____

2. The boy will read. (Add a direct object.)

____

3. The boy will tell about the book. (Add an indirect object.)

____

4. The teacher will give a good grade. (Add an indirect object.)

____

5. The classroom has a desk a chalkboard and a clock. (Add punctuation.)

____

Verb Tenses

- A verb in the **present tense** tells what happens now.
- In the present tense, you must have **subject-verb agreement**. Add *-s* to most verbs if the subject is singular. Do not add *-s* if the subject is plural or *I* or *you*.

Rewrite each sentence below, using the correct present-tense verb in parentheses.

1. Belinda (slap, slaps) boys and (grind, grinds) their faces into the grass.

____

2. Robert (witness, witnesses) Belinda staring down the janitor's pit bull.

____

3. The class (rehearse, rehearses) the play about the Donner party for three weeks.

____

4. Robert's classmates (think, thinks) he looks great in the red beard.

____

5. The beard (make, makes) Robert sneeze.

____

6. Most of the students (do, does) not have speaking parts.

____

7. Only those who score twelve or more out of fifteen on spelling tests (have, has) lines to say.

____

8. Mrs. Bunnin (tell, tells) the class to speak loudly.

____

9. Students playing trees and snowflakes (hum, hums) to create the sound effects of a storm.

____

10. When he practices at home, Robert's line (come, comes) easily and naturally.

____

Extension: Have students write a paragraph about a play or another kind of school presentation that they were involved in. Tell them to use present tense verbs and to make sure that each verb agrees with the subject.

Verb Tenses

- A verb in the **past tense** tells about an action that already happened.
- Add *-ed* to most verbs to show past tense.
- A verb in the **future tense** tells about an action that is going to happen.
- To write about the future, use the special verb *will*.

Write the verb in parentheses in the past tense.

1. Roberto (want) ____________ scientists to rely on him for his memory.

2. The three weeks of play rehearsal (pass) ____________ much too quickly.

3. Roberto (pick) ____________ up a dollar bill lying on the street.

4. The actors (dress) ____________ in their costumes after lunch.

5. Roberto (whisper) ____________ his line over and over to himself.

6. Roberto's words (seem) ____________ to get caught in his beard.

7. Belinda (warn) ____________ him not to make a mistake.

8. Roberto (stagger) ____________ to the center of the stage.

Change the following verbs into the future tense.

9. build ____________

10. leave ____________

11. buzz ____________

12. remove ____________

Extension: Ask students to write sentences for the four verbs in the future tense above. Then have them turn the verbs into past tense and write sentences for each.

Verb Tenses

- A verb in the **present tense** tells what happens now.
- In the present tense, you must have **subject-verb agreement**. Add *-s* to most verbs if the subject is singular. Do not add *-s* if the subject is plural or *I* or *you*.
- A verb in the **past tense** tells about an action that already happened.
- Add *-ed* to most verbs to show past tense.
- A verb in the **future tense** tells about an action that is going to happen.
- To write about the future, use the special verb *will*.

Identify the tense of the verbs in the following sentences as *present, past,* or *future*.

______________ **1.** Mrs. Bunnin's class reads about famous events in history.

______________ **2.** Tomorrow they will discuss the Donner party.

______________ **3.** Mrs. Bunnin cares about how well the students do in their play.

______________ **4.** Yesterday the actors dressed in their costumes for a final rehearsal.

______________ **5.** They will help each other remember their lines.

______________ **6.** They learned about how difficult traveling was during the days of the Old West.

______________ **7.** During rehearsals they practice their lines over and over.

______________ **8.** Someday perhaps one of the students will appear in another play.

______________ **9.** The students enjoyed the play.

______________ **10.** Roberto will try out for another play soon.

______________ **11.** Mrs. Bunnin likes the students' work.

______________ **12.** We needed time for more rehearsals.

Extension: Have students identify present, past, and future tense verbs in a newspaper or magazine article. Then have them identify the subjects of the sentences.

Name ______________________ Date ____________

Spelling Changes

- If a verb ends in *s, ch, sh, x,* or *z*, add *-es* in the present with a singular subject.
- If a verb ends with a consonant and *y*, change *y* to *i* and add *-es* for present or *-ed* for past.
- If a verb ends with *e*, drop the *e* and add *-ed* for past.
- If a verb ends with one vowel and one consonant, double the consonant before adding *-ed* for past.

Rewrite each of the following sentences by changing the verb to the tense shown in parentheses.

1. The class rehearses the play for three weeks. (past tense)

____

2. The janitor's dog licks his chops. (past tense)

____

3. Mrs. Bunnin carried a large box. (present tense)

____

4. Mrs. Bunnin rolls her eyes at Roberto. (past tense)

____

5. The boys will study their lines after school. (past tense)

____

6. Several friends try out for parts in the play. (past tense)

____

7. Mrs. Bunnin will arrange the actors on stage. (present tense)

____

8. After lunch the students scurry onto the stage. (past tense)

____

Extension: Have students make flash cards with a present-tense verb on one side and its past-tense form on the other. Have students then work in pairs to quiz each other in spelling the past-tense form.

Verb Tenses

Circle the letter of the choice that corrects each numbered sentence. If there is no error in the sentence, circle *c* for *correct*.

1. Tomorrow Tim learn a new role.
- **a.** Tomorrow Tim learned a new role.
- **b.** Tomorrow Tim will learn a new role.
- **c.** correct

2. Pamela cried at the play's sad ending.
- **a.** Pamela cry at the play's sad ending.
- **b.** Tonight Pamela cry at the play's sad ending.
- **c.** correct

3. Yesterday the Powells watch their daughter's performance.
- **a.** Yesterday the Powells watched their daughter's performance.
- **b.** Yesterday the Powells will watch their daughter's performance.
- **c.** correct

4. Before yesterday's performance, no one guessed that Jane was talented.
- **a.** Before yesterday's performance, no one guess that Jane was talented.
- **b.** Before yesterday's performance, no one will guess that Jane was talented.
- **c.** correct

5. At the end of the play, the audience clap and shouted until they were hoarse.
- **a.** At the end of the play, the audience clapped and shout until they were hoarse.
- **b.** At the end of the play, the audience clapped and shouted until they were hoarse.
- **c.** correct

6. Carolee brush her long red hair in her role as Rapunzel.
- **a.** Carolee brushes her long red hair in her role as Rapunzel.
- **b.** Carolee brushs her long red hair in her role as Rapunzel.
- **c.** correct

Verb Tenses

- In the present tense, you must have **subject-verb agreement**. Add *-s* to most verbs if the subject is singular. Do not add *-s* if the subject is plural or *I* or *you*.
- A verb in the **past tense** tells about an action that already happened.
- Add *-ed* to most verbs to show past tense.
- A verb in the **future tense** tells about an action that is going to happen.
- To write about the future, use the special verb *will*.

Mechanics:

- If a verb ends in *s, ch, sh, x,* or *z*, add *-es* in the present with a singular subject.
- If a verb ends with a consonant and *y*, change *y* to *i* and add *-es* for present or *-ed* for past.
- If a verb ends with *e*, drop the *e* and add *-ed* for past.
- If a verb ends with one vowel and one consonant, double the consonant before adding *-ed* for past.

Read each sentence aloud. Correct the spelling of the verbs and their tenses.

1. Yesterday the stagehand promise to fix the curtain by Monday.

____

2. A student mixs the paint for the scenery.

____

3. Someone carryed the props onto the stage.

____

4. Otis and Loretta will perform Act III for the first time last weekend.

____

5. The program show a scene from Act I.

____

6. The actors rehearse all day yesterday.

____

Name ______________________ Date ____________

Main and Helping Verbs

- A **verb phrase** is made up of a main verb and one or more helping verbs. A **helping verb** helps the main verb show an action or make a statement.
- Common helping verbs are *am, are, is, was, were, have, has, had, do, does, did, be, being, been, will, shall, can, could, would, should, might, must.*

Write the verb phrases in the following sentences.

1. Banzar had always wanted to be a musician. ______________________

2. Swanga and Taki are initiated into manhood. ______________________

3. Banzar is forced to leave his home and family. ______________________

4. The whole family must listen to the wisdom of the elders. ______________________

5. Banzar realizes that he might not see his family again. ______________________

6. Sholo and Banzar will travel together to Otolo. ______________________

7. Sholo promises Banzar that he will teach him important skills.

____

8. Banzar knows that he is talking with his brothers. ______________________

9. Banzar must tell his people about the past so they will be strong in the future.

____

10. He knows that this is what Sholo would want him to do.

____

11. The king promises that Banzar will be handsomely rewarded.

____

12. The king likes Banzar better than all the other musicians he has heard.

____

Extension: Have students choose 5 of the helping verbs listed in the box and use them to write sentences.

Verb Tenses

- Main and helping verbs form different verb tenses.

Tense	Example
Present perfect	I have walked
Past perfect	I had walked
Present progressive	I am walking
Past progressive	I was walking
Future progressive	I will be walking

Name the tense of each of the following verbs.

1. walk ____________________

2. has used ____________________

3. cared ____________________

4. seems ____________________

5. had marked ____________________

6. will be fixing ____________________

7. depended ____________________

8. am helping ____________________

Write the form shown in parentheses for the verb in each of the sentences.

9. I wait. (present progressive)

____

10. We waited here before. (past perfect)

____

11. I will wait for Miguel for a long while. (future progressive)

____

12. I waited for Maria. (past progressive)

____

Extension: Have students choose four of the eight verbs above and write sentences for them.

Main and Helping Verbs

- A verb phrase is made up of a main verb and one or more helping verbs. A **helping verb** helps the main verb show an action or make a statement.
- Common helping verbs are *am, are, is, was, were, have, has, had, do, does, did, be, being, been, will, shall, can, could, would, should, might, must.*
- Main and helping verbs form different verb tenses.

Tense	**Example**
Present perfect	I have walked
Past perfect	I had walked
Present progressive	I am walking
Past progressive	I was walking
Future progressive	I will be walking

Identify the tense of each underlined verb in the following sentences.

1. For many years the term *griot* <u>has been used</u> to describe West African storytellers.

____

2. However, many storytellers <u>have come</u> to associate the term with the French, who <u>had colonized</u> Sierra Leone.

____

3. Storytellers <u>prefer</u> the term *finah*, which combines the roles of orator, inspirational speaker, and master of ceremonies.

____

4. In five years, finahs <u>will</u> probably <u>be using</u> computers alongside their drums.

____

5. One story <u>tells</u> about a town in Sierra Leone that <u>had grown</u> up around a great tree, 20 feet in width.

____

6. Everyone in the town <u>was working</u> hard.

____

7. By this time tomorrow, the Farrells <u>will be flying</u> somewhere over West Africa.

____

8. Jessica <u>had arrived</u> by the time her parents got home from work.

____

Extension: Have students write a short paragraph about teaching someone how to do something. Remind them to use correct tenses in their paragraph.

Name ______________________ Date ______________

Contractions

- A contraction is a shortened form of two words.
- A contraction can be made by combining a verb with the word *not.*
- An apostrophe (') shows that the letter *o* has been left out.

These contractions are formed from helping verbs. In each case, the apostrophe replaces the letter *o* in *not.*

isn't = is not	doesn't = does not	mustn't = must not
won't = will not	couldn't = could not	

Write the contractions for the following helping verbs and *not.*

1. are not ______________

2. have not ______________

3. was not ______________

4. were not ______________

5. has not ______________

Fill in the blanks in the following sentences with the correct contraction of a helping verb and *not.* Be sure to put the apostrophe in the right place.

6. Banzar ______________ want to be a farmer or blacksmith.

7. He ______________ interested in selling things at the marketplace.

8. The elders of the village ______________ happy with Banzar.

9. Music ______________ grow yams to fill the stomach.

10. Banzar ______________ stop playing his flute.

Extension: Have students write the rules for a new game or sport that they would like to see introduced to the Olympics. Tell them to use contractions made up of helping verbs and *not* in their list of rules.

Name ______________________ Date ____________ TEST **Grammar** 81

Verb Tenses

Rewrite each underlined verb in the tense given in parentheses.

1. He study music before he left the village. (past perfect)

____

2. The storytellers construct their tales from actual events. (past)

____

3. She ask the elders for advice. (present)

____

4. By the time we were adults, I become a storyteller. (past perfect)

____

5. I heard that song before. (present perfect)

____

Name ______________________ Date ______________ MORE PRACTICE **Grammar** **82**

Verb Tenses

- A **verb phrase** is made up of a main verb and one or more helping verbs. A **helping verb** helps the main verb show an action or make a statement.
- Common helping verbs are *am, are, is, was, were, have, has, had, do, does, did, be, being, been, will, shall, can, could, would, should, might, must.*
- Main and helping verbs form different verb tenses.

Mechanics

- A contraction is a shortened form of two words.
- A contraction can be made by combining a verb with the word *not.*
- An apostrophe (') shows that the letter *o* has been left out.

Work with a partner. One of you should read the sentences aloud, while the other proofreads. Listen for the sentences that have missing or incorrect helping verbs or contractions. Write the corrected sentences on the lines. The proofreader then reads the corrected sentences aloud.

1. Banzar's brothers was'nt jealous of his good fortune.

____

2. Banzar's father have recognized the song his son sang.

____

3. Banzar's brother claims that his younger brother woodn't work.

____

4. The king of Lagos tells Banzar that if he remain in the country, he will be handsomely rewarded.

____

____

5. Banzar's brothers doesnt recognize him.

____

Linking Verbs

- A **linking verb** does not show action. It links the subject to a noun or an adjective in the predicate.
- Common linking verbs are *am, is, are, was, were, be, being, been, seem, feel, appear, become, look, taste, smell.*

In the provided space, write the linking verb in each of the following sentences.

1. Limestone is a soft rock. ____________

2. Exploring caves can be dangerous. ____________

3. It is easy to get lost or stuck in a cave. ____________

4. The cave seems enormous. ____________

5. The scientists felt good about their discovery. ____________

6. The walls of the cave look like an art gallery. ____________

7. The art appears as animals. ____________

8. Handprints are common in caves. ____________

9. The reason for the handprints seems a mystery. ____________

10. Few human figures appear in cave art. ____________

Extension: Have students determine whether the subjects in the ten sentences above are singular or plural.

Name ______________________ Date ____________

Linking Verbs

- A **predicate noun** follows a linking verb and renames or identifies the subject.
- A **predicate adjective** follows a linking verb and describes the subject.

In the space provided, write the predicate nouns or predicate adjectives in the following sentences. Also, identify the word as a predicate noun or a predicate adjective.

1. The scientists felt energetic. ______________________
2. Wall art was the work of Stone Age painters. ______________________
3. One of the scientists is a source of new information about the cave painters.

   ____
4. The paintings seem preserved. ______________________
5. Many of the animals are now extinct. ______________________
6. The names of the artists are unknown. ______________________
7. The drawings look old. ______________________
8. The scientists could be next year's prize winners. ______________________
9. The paintings are a reminder of our long history. ______________________
10. The animals look beautiful on the walls. ______________________

Extension: Have students pretend what they will be like thirty years from today. Tell them to write a paragraph with linking verbs describing what they will look and feel like, what they will have done with their lives, and what they still hope to accomplish.

Name ________________________ Date ____________

Linking Verbs

- A **linking verb** does not show action. It links the subject to a noun or an adjective in the predicate.
- Common linking verbs are *am, is, are, was, were, be, being, been, seem, feel, appear, become, look, taste, smell.*
- A **predicate noun** follows a linking verb and renames or identifies the subject.
- A **predicate adjective** follows a linking verb and describes the subject.

In the space provided, write the linking verbs or verb phrases in the following sentences. Then identify the words that the verb links.

1. Some of the animals were gentle creatures. ____________________
2. Jean-Marie Chauvet has been an explorer for many years.
____
3. The designs on the walls are complicated. ____________________
4. The eyes of the animals seem alive. ____________________
5. Some of the painters could have been professionals. ____________________
____
6. The job of a cave explorer can be very dangerous. ____________________
____
7. The story must have been true. ____________________
8. Cave paintings are living history. ____________________
9. The explorer seemed uneasy. ____________________
10. The paintings will remain a reminder of early humans. ____________________
____

/10

Extension: Tell students to write a mystery story using as many linking verbs as possible. Once the stories are complete, have students exchange papers and identify the linking verbs, predicate nouns, and predicate adjectives.

Letter Punctuation

- Use a colon after the greeting in a business letter.
- Use a comma after the closing.
- Use a comma between the names of a city and a state.
- Use a comma between the day and year in a date.

Proofread this business letter for errors in colons and commas.

1233 Bellerock Street
Pittsburgh Pennsylvania 15217

Mr. Jean-Marie Chauvet
Sorbonne University
Paris France

August 12 2001

Dear Mr. Chauvet
I recently read an article about your 1994 discovery. I am interested in learning more about the cave paintings near Avignon France.

The article made me curious. Did you ever find out what the handprints stood for? Is there a story about the designs on the walls? I really would like to know more about what you learned. Could you suggest some articles or books that will tell me more?

I know you must be very busy, but I hope you will take just a few minutes to respond to my letter.

Sincerely
Jason Guttman

Extension: Have students write a business letter about a product that did not work or fit. Remind them to use colons and commas in the correct places.

Name ______________________________ Date ____________

Linking Verbs

Circle the letter of the choice that corrects each numbered sentence. If there is no error in the sentence, circle *c* for *correct.*

1. The cave drawings looks exciting.

a. The cave drawings look exciting.

b. The cave drawings are looking exciting.

c. correct

2. People have grown more aware of cave art.

a. People has grown more aware of cave art.

b. People are grown more aware of cave art.

c. correct

3. The animals looks real.

a. The animals look real.

b. The animals looking real

c. correct

4. The scientists growed impatient as they neared the cave.

a. The scientists grows impatient as they neared the cave.

b. The scientists grew impatient as they neared the cave.

c. correct

5. The howling of the coyotes sounds distant.

a. The howling of the coyotes sound distant.

b. The howling of the coyotes have sounded distant.

c. correct

6. The animals in the paintings seem friendly.

a. The animals in the painting seeming friendly.

b. The animals in the painting are seemed friendly.

c. correct

Linking Verbs

- A **linking verb** does not show action. It links the subject to a noun or an adjective in the predicate.
- Common linking verbs are *am, is, are, was, were, be, being, been, seem, feel, appear, become, look, taste, smell.*
- A **predicate noun** follows a linking verb and renames or identifies the subject.
- A **predicate adjective** follows a linking verb and describes the subject.

Mechanics:

- Use a colon after the greeting in a business letter.
- Use a comma after the closing.
- Use a comma between the names of a city and a state.
- Use a comma between the day and year in a date.

The writer of this letter did not proofread for mistakes. Read the letter and then correct any mistakes made with linking verbs, colons, and commas.

508 Constitution Avenue
Washington D.C. 14088

Mr. Jeffrey Arneault
Director
National Museum
1456 Pennsylvania Avenue
Washington D.C. 14088

January 23 2002

Dear Mr. Arneault

Thank you very much for taking the time to show Ms. Hile's class around the museum last Monday, January 16. We was particularly impressed with the display of French cave paintings. The slide presentation seem to add detail and focus to what we have been studying. Our behind-the-scenes tour were also fascinating. It gave us a chance to see what lies behind the professional displays. Miss Hile and the rest of the class agree that it was a fascinating and worthwhile day.

Sincerely

Leann Polster

Name ______________________________ Date ____________ LEARN **Grammar** 89

Irregular Verbs

- An **irregular verb** is a verb that does not add *-ed* to form the past tense.

Present	**Past**
speak	spoke
choose	chose
drink	drank
know	knew
wear	wore
teach	taught
blow	blew
break	broke
freeze	froze
catch	caught
sink	sank
tear	tore
think	thought

Correct errors in verb tenses in the following sentences.

1. Musical notes breaked the silence of the mountains. ____________

2. Neanderthals may have knowed about music. ____________

3. The questions beginned when a paleontologist finded a bone. ____________________

4. Neanderthals blowed single notes through holes in the wood. ____________

5. Other scientists thinked that the bone was just an old chewed stick. ____________

6. They catched sight of some stone tools that the Neanderthals maked.

____

Extension: Have students pick out other irregular verbs from a newspaper or magazine article and add them to the chart.

Name ______________________________ Date ______________

Irregular Verbs

- Some irregular verbs have special spellings when used with the helping verbs *have, has, or had.*

Present	**Past**	**Past** (*with have, has, or had*)
speak	spoke	spoken
choose	chose	chosen
drink	drank	drunk
know	knew	known
wear	wore	worn
teach	taught	taught
blow	blew	blown
break	broke	broken
freeze	froze	frozen
catch	caught	caught
sink	sank	sunk
tear	tore	torn
think	thought	thought

Each sentence contains an incorrect form of an irregular verb. Write the correct verb.

1. Scientist Bonnie Blackwell knowed all about early musical instruments.

____

2. She thinked that air could pass through the hollow bone. _________________

3. She had speaked with other scientists about the age of the bone.

____

4. Scientists finded the bones of Lucy, a 3 million year old apelike creature.

____

5. The bones of now extinct animals probably freezed in the ground.

____

Extension: Have students choose five verbs from the chart and write sentences for each, showing the correct spelling of the tenses.

Irregular Verbs

- An **irregular verb** is a verb that does not add *-ed* to form the past tense.
- Some irregular verbs have special spellings when used with the helping verbs *have, has,* or *had.*

Write the correct form (past or past participle) of the verb given in parentheses.

1. The scientist ____________ the bone may have been a flute. (think)

2. An animal bite may have ____________ the bone. (break)

3. The pond has ____________ over twice this winter. (freeze)

4. She ____________ to the other scientists. (speak)

5. Last year my older sister ____________ us how to play a flute. (teach)

6. A Neanderthal may have ____________ into the bone to make music. (blow)

7. I wonder if Neanderthals ____________ into the bone to make music. (blow)

8. This new finding may have changed what some scientists ____________ about Neanderthals. (think)

Extension: For answers that are in the past participle, have students recast the sentence and write the verb in the past. For answers that are in the past, have students recast the sentence and write the verb in the past participle.

Commas

- Use a comma to show a pause after an introductory word, such as *well.*
- Use commas to set off words that interrupt the flow of thought in a sentence, such as *of course.*
- Use commas to set off nouns of direct address.

Insert commas where they are needed in the following sentences.

1. No Neanderthals looked more like human beings than apes.

2. Of course everyone wants to know what the bone is and where it came from.

3. The theory in my opinion is weak and unclear.

4. The bone on the other hand could have come from any animal.

5. The bone I think came from a bear's leg.

6. No Carmen your answer I'm sorry to say isn't correct.

7. To come right to the point Dr. Turk we don't agree with your theory.

8. Yes it was Beverly Lau I think who was the student member of the team.

9. Why Mr. Neanderthal what beautiful music you play!

10. When I finished reading however I was still not convinced.

Extension: Give students a list of interrupters like the following: after all, for example, by the way, furthermore, besides, in fact, to tell the truth, in my opinion, in addition, and as I was saying. Have them write five sentences, experimenting with the placement of the interrupter. Remind them to use commas correctly to set off these expressions.

Name ______________________ Date ____________ TEST Grammar 93

Irregular Verbs

Write the past tense of each verb below.

1. drink ____________
2. blow ____________
3. think ____________
4. wear ____________

Use the past participle of each verb in a sentence of your own.

5. speak ______________________________
6. sink ______________________________
7. know ______________________________
8. freeze ______________________________

Irregular Verbs

- An **irregular verb** is a verb that does not add *-ed* to form the past tense.
- Some irregular verbs have special spellings when used with the helping verbs *have, has,* or *had.*

Mechanics:

- Use a comma to show a pause after an introductory word, such as *well.*
- Use commas to set off words that interrupt the flow of thought in a sentence, such as *of course.*
- Use commas to set off nouns of direct address.

Rewrite the sentences. Use the correct form of the irregular verb and insert commas where they are needed.

1. Neanderthal people speaked in grunts Carol.

____

2. They knowed I think how to make music.

____

3. Of course Dr. Blackwell thinked the bone was a flute.

____

4. Hey other scientists have choose to believe that the holes were made by a chewing animal.

____

____

5. They thinked after all that a wolf's teeth made the holes.

____

6. Pat have you teached students about Stone Age music?

____

Verbs

Read the passage and look at each underlined word. How would you describe the word? Circle the letter of your answer.

> Calvin has unusual vision. He sees <u>colors</u> (1). He rides a bike. He has friends. He is blind, but he deals with it. His parents give <u>him</u> (2) confidence.

1. **A.** active verb
   B. direct object
   C. indirect object
   D. subject

2. **F.** active verb
   G. direct object
   H. indirect object
   J. predicate

Read the passage and look at the underlined sentences. Is there a mistake? If there is, how do you correct it? Circle the letter of your answer.

> <u>The play tell the story of the Donner party. These people tried to travel across the country in wagons. Winter caught them high in the mountains.</u> (3) <u>Many of them died from hunger. Robert will play the part of one of the settlers. Other students make sounds to imitate the wind</u> (4). <u>Their teacher worries that they will forget their lines. She applaud loudly when they finish the play.</u> (5)

3. **A.** Change *tell* to *tells.*
   B. Change *tried* to *try.*
   C. Change *caught* to *will catch.*
   D. No mistake.

4. **F.** Change *died* to *will die.*
   G. Change *will play* to *played.*
   H. Change *make* to *will make.*
   J. No mistake.

5. **A.** Change *worries* to *worry.*
   B. Change *will forget* to *forgot.*
   C. Change *applaud* to *applauds.*
   D. No mistake.

Verbs

Read the passage and look at the underlined sentences. Is there a mistake? If there is, how do you correct it? Circle the letter of your answer.

> Sholo had played before kings all his life. He and other praise singers has kept the songs of Africa alive. (6) One day as he was walking to Otolo, Sholo met Banzar. Since then, they had become good friends. Sholo has taught Banzar to earn his living as a musician. (7) Now, Banzar is walking the roads alone from village to village. He is reminding people of their past. He has been remembered as a great musician. (8)

6. A. Change *had played* to *have played.*
   B. Change *has kept* to *had kept.*
   C. Change *was walking* to *is walking.*
   D. Change *met* to *is meeting.*

7. F. Change *had become* to *have become.*
   G. Change *had become* to *are become.*
   H. Change *has taught* to *have taught.*
   J. Change *has taught* to *had taught.*

8. A. Change *is walking* to *has walked.*
   B. Change *is reminding* to *have reminded.*
   C. Change *is reminding* to *had reminded.*
   D. Change *has been remembered* to *will be remembered.*

Read the passage and look at each underlined word. How would you describe the word? Circle the letter of your answer.

> The painters at Chauvet were modern humans (9). They lived thousands of years ago, and little is really known about them. We do know their paintings are colorful (10). They capture the beauty and movement of the animals the artists saw daily.

9. A. Linking verb
   B. Helping verb
   C. Predicate noun
   D. Predicate adjective

10. F. Linking verb
    G. Helping verb
    H. Predicate noun
    J. Predicate adjective

Name ______________________ Date ____________ LEARN **Grammar** **97**

Adjectives

- An **adjective** is a word that modifies, or describes, a noun or pronoun and tells *what kind, how many*, or *which one*.
- A **predicate adjective** follows a linking verb and describes the subject.

Underline each adjective in the following sentences. (Some sentences have more than one adjective.)

1. Egyptians wanted to save royal mummies from greedy robbers.
2. Priests moved the mummies to an abandoned tomb.
3. The burial place was hidden for three thousand years.
4. Bodies of ancient rulers were wrapped in linen bandages.
5. The tomb had four rooms with painted walls.
6. The dusty chamber was filled with noble statues.
7. Gilded statues of animals gazed upon the eager but cautious visitors.

Circle each predicate adjective in the following sentences. (Some sentences have more than one predicate adjective.)

8. Lord Carnarvon's excavations were expensive.
9. The artifacts looked rare and valuable.
10. The little canary in the cage seemed friendly.
11. To Howard Carter, the huts appeared old and uninhabited.
12. The discovery of Tutankhamen's tomb was incredible, historic, and wonderful.

Extension: Ask students to review the visuals that accompany this selection in their books. Have them use adjectives and predicate adjectives to write interpretations of or responses to several visuals.

Demonstrative Adjectives

- A **demonstrative adjective** points out something and tells *which one* or *which ones.*
- Use *this* and *that* with singular nouns. Use *these* and *those* with plural nouns.
- *This* and *these* refer to nouns that are nearby; *that* and *those* refer to nouns that are farther away.

Study the demonstrative adjectives in parentheses. Write the demonstrative adjective that correctly completes each sentence.

1. ____________ golden earrings once belonged to Queen Hatshepsut. (These, This)
2. The archaeologist received ____________ award for his work. (these, this)
3. ____________ vase has a floral design. (These, That)
4. Would you hand me ____________ museum tickets? (those, that)
5. ____________ artifact is the most interesting one in the collection. (This, Those)

Complete each sentence with an appropriate demonstrative adjective.

6. The king's mummy wore ____________ mask of solid gold.
7. Priests hid ____________ precious jewels in the pharaoh's burial cloth.
8. Do you want to visit ____________ temple of the New Kingdom?
9. Howard Carter's canary was eaten by ____________ poisonous snake.
10. The hasty thieves lost ____________ gold rings.

Extension: Have students write a description of Tutankhamen's tomb using demonstrative adjectives in every sentence. Students might enjoy exchanging and comparing their sentences to see which details are mentioned most often.

Using Adjectives

- An **adjective** is a word that modifies, or describes, a noun or pronoun and tells *what kind, how many*, or *which one.*
- A **predicate adjective** follows a linking verb and describes the subject.
- A **demonstrative adjective** points out something and tells *which one* or *which ones.*

Underline each adjective once and predicate adjective twice in these sentences. (Some sentences have more than one adjective.)

1. Eager tourists can view rare artifacts from the time of the pharaohs.

2. The old coffin felt heavy and awkward.

3. According to knowledgeable historians, Tutankhamen was unimportant.

4. A museum in Cairo is famous for its extensive collection.

5. Do you believe the story about an evil curse on the royal tombs?

6. Howard Carter seemed speechless at the huge golden treasure.

7. What a magnificent discovery he made!

Write the demonstrative adjective that correctly completes each sentence.

8. What happened to ____________ two grave-robbing brothers? (this, those)

9. ____________ mummies are preserved in the Museum of Cairo. (These, That)

10. She bought ____________ water jar in the bazaar. (that, these)

11. I will not sell you ____________ papyrus scroll. (those, this)

12. Merchants sell ____________ wood carvings at the street market. (these, this)

Extension: Ask groups of students to write and present a speech that guides might give as they conduct a tour of the Mummy Room at the Cairo Museum. Have students use a variety of regular, predicate, and demonstrative adjectives in their speeches.

Proper Adjectives

- A **proper adjective** is formed from a proper noun.
- A proper adjective begins with a capital letter.

On the line provided, write the proper adjective in each sentence.

1. These Cairo exhibits are among the country's greatest tourist attractions.

   ____

2. Our class clown asked, "Do Egyptian mummies have daddies?" ______________

3. It took a Herculean effort to pry the doors open. ______________

4. Egypt is located on the southern Mediterranean coast. ______________

5. Did you know that Egypt is a North African country? ______________

6. Many students in Egypt learn the English language. ______________

7. A special exhibit about Tutankhamen toured many American museums.

   ____

8. Its New York showing attracted crowds every day. ______________

9. Americans treated the dead king almost like a Hollywood star. ______________

10. A famous Shakespearean actor played the pharaoh in a play. ______________

Extension: Have students write five sentences using proper adjectives.

Adjectives

Decide which word in the sentence is the adjective. Circle the letter of your answer.

1. Curious tourists visit the Valley of the Kings.
   - **a.** curious
   - **b.** of
   - **c.** visit
   - **d.** tourists

2. The military weapons belong in the tomb of Ramses VI.
   - **a.** in
   - **b.** belong
   - **c.** military
   - **d.** Ramses VI

3. The archeologist digs in this pit.
   - **a.** archeologist
   - **b.** digs
   - **c.** in
   - **d.** this

4. The bandages used to wrap kings are ragged.
   - **a.** bandages
   - **b.** used
   - **c.** are
   - **d.** ragged

5. The author of *Mummies, Tombs, and Treasure* has written fifteen books.
   - **a.** The
   - **b.** fifteen
   - **c.** has
   - **d.** author

6. James and his friend enjoy learning about foreign lands.
   - **a.** about
   - **b.** friend
   - **c.** foreign
   - **d.** his

7. This historian tells the story of Egypt.
   - **a.** This
   - **b.** Egypt
   - **c.** of
   - **d.** tells

8. I want to make these reservations for our hotel.
   - **a.** hotel
   - **b.** these
   - **c.** want
   - **d.** I

/8

Working with Adjectives

- An **adjective** is a word that modifies, or describes, a noun or pronoun and tells *what kind, how many*, or *which one.*
- A **predicate adjective** follows a linking verb and describes the subject.
- A **demonstrative adjective** points out something and tells *which one* or *which ones.*

Mechanics:

- A proper adjective is formed from a proper noun and begins with a capital letter.

Underline the adjectives in the following sentences. Identify each adjective as *adjective, predicate adjective, demonstrative adjective, or proper adjective.*

1. A Roman architect imitated designs on the wall of the tomb. ______________

2. Farmers once used these beads as a form of money. ______________

3. Regal tombs intrigue archeologists who are interested in the history of Egypt.

____

4. Those shells were found in the Amenhotep tomb. ______________

5. Henry was eager to read a book on archeology. ______________

6. Anyone can learn about this career if they have access to the Internet.

____

7. The wall was beautiful with its scenes of water lilies and the river.

____

8. The golden colors dazzle the eyes. ______________

Articles

- The words *a, an*, and *the* are special adjectives called **articles**.
- Use *a* and *an* with singular nouns.
- Use *a* if the next word starts with a consonant sound.
- Use *an* if the next word starts with a vowel sound.

Study the pair of articles in each sentence. Underline the article that correctly completes the sentence.

1. Julie and Martin have (a, an) detailed map of the North Pole.

2. (A, The) sled dogs fell into the icy water.

3. What (a, an) icy wind blew across the Arctic!

4. Minus 4 degrees is (a, an) warm day in this barren land.

5. Seven powerful dogs pull (an, the) snow sled across the ice.

6. Does the team of scientists eat (a, the) same meal every day?

7. A sled dog can be (a, an) ally in a snowstorm.

Complete each sentence with the correct article—*a, an,* or *the.*

8. The snow team keeps __________ schedule of chores to share.

9. If __________ dogs do not get enough exercise, they become hard to control.

10. Of course, __________ avalanche always is possible.

11. You can learn about Arctic travelers on __________ Internet.

12. Will takes __________ intense interest in his scientific work, doesn't he?

Extension: Have students draw an arrow from each article in the sentence above to the noun it modifies. Pairs of students might exchange papers and check each other's answers.

Working with *The*

- Use *the* with singular nouns that name a particular person, place, or thing.
- Use *the* before all plural nouns.

Select the correct articles from the choices in parentheses. Rewrite each sentence with the correct article or articles.

1. Takako made (a, an) small hole in (the, a) ice.

____

2. Can you name (a, the) one lead dog in your pack?

____

3. That winter sunset casts (an, a) orange glow across (an, the) horizon.

____

4. Julie and Takako use (a, an) pickax to chop (an, the) ice off their sled runners.

____

5. If you were (an, a) scientist, would you travel to (a, the) North Pole?

____

6. Is (a, an) unused battery kept warm in Julie's sleeping bag?

____

7. (A, The) international team named (a, the) communication system "Esmerelda."

____

8. What were (the, an) emotions that Julie felt as she cried, "Mush!" to (a, the) dogs?

____

Extension: Ask groups of students to choose five sentences from the exercise and write a response or other companion piece for each one. Have them discuss and verify their use of articles.

Articles

- The words *a, an*, and *the* are special adjectives called **articles**.
- Use *a* and *an* with singular nouns. Use *a* if the next word starts with a consonant sound. Use *an* if the next word starts with a vowel sound.
- Use *the* with singular nouns that name a particular person, place, or thing. Use *the* before all plural nouns.

Change the article in parentheses so that it correctly completes each sentence. Then rewrite each sentence.

1. Shaklee became (an) hero of the day.

____

2. It is (a) unlikely job for someone who hates cold weather.

____

3. (A) expedition members headed for the Canadian coast.

____

4. (The) incredibly cold night occurred in April.

____

5. Cochise jumps at (an) falling snowflake.

____

6. Victor uses (an) harpoonlike pole to measure ice thickness.

____

7. On (a) day of May 17, Will knew that they would not reach Resolute.

____

8. Riding across (an) Arctic Ocean takes (an) strength of (the) athlete.

____

Extension: Have students pretend they are members of the Arctic team. Ask them to write and share a journal entry, using at least ten articles.

Colons

- Use a colon to separate the hour and the minute in the time of day.
- Use a colon to introduce a list of items that ends a sentence.
- Use a colon after the greeting of a business letter.

The writer of this letter didn't check for mistakes. As you read the letter, correct any colon errors you find.

P.O. Box 15

Mammoth Lakes, CA 93546

June 5, 2000

Dear Mr. Castor

I have been working since the sun rose over the mountain ridge at 5 56 A.M. Today I have scheduled three duties for the team identify our route, take temperature readings, and sort our food. Our day will end at 6 30 P.M. Then I will return to my tent and attend to the following business matters answering mail, taking inventory of tools, and ordering supplies.

I look forward to a return letter.

Sincerely,

William Sarno

Extension: Have pairs of students write a letter to a member of the Arctic team about whom they have read. Have them include three colons in the letter.

Articles

Circle the correct article in the following sentences. Some sentences have more than one article.

1. (An, A) computer sends information about the North Pole to (a, the) students.
2. Pulling sleds from the icy water is (an, a) risky job.
3. (An, A) awestruck crew looked at (the, an) 20-foot-tall wall of ice.
4. (The, A) ice block shattered into (a, an) hundred pieces.
5. After (a, an) long day, (a, the) dogs enjoy (a, an) restful nap.
6. They hoped they would not get caught in (a, an) windstorm.
7. (A, An) member of (an, the) team loaded (an, the) sled with supplies.
8. We drove to (the, an) mountain ridge and peered over its side.
9. The explorers used (a, an) new computer and transmitter called Charlie.
10. We grew concerned when (a, an) anxious polar bear stared down at us.

___ /10

Practicing With Articles and Colons

- The words *a, an*, and *the* are special adjectives called articles.
- Use *a* and *an* with singular nouns.
- Use *a* if the next word starts with a consonant sound.
- Use *an* if the next word starts with a vowel sound.
- Use *the* with singular nouns that name a particular person, place, or thing.
- Use *the* before all plural nouns.

Mechanics

- Use a colon to separate the hour and the minute in the time of day.
- Use a colon to introduce a list of items that ends a sentence.
- Use a colon after the greeting of a business letter.

Read the following letter aloud. Then rewrite it, correcting misused articles and inserting colons in the appropriate places.

42 Lincoln Street
Costa Mesa, CA 92626
April 3, 2000

Dear Mr. Kim

My plane flight arrives at 742 P.M. on April 29. I have arranged for an car to drive me to an hotel in Anchorage. I will bring with me a following materials an topical map, an pocket calculator, and a extra heavy jacket. My flight home is scheduled for 830 A.M. an week later.

I am looking forward to working with an team.

Sincerely,
Linda Miller

Name ______________________ Date ____________ LEARN **Grammar** 109

Comparative and Superlative Adjectives

- The **comparative** form of an adjective compares two nouns.
- The **superlative** form compares more than two nouns.
- Add *-er* or *-est* to most one-syllable and some two-syllable adjectives to form the comparative or superlative.

Write the comparing forms of the following adjectives.

	Compares two nouns	Compares more than two nouns
1. cool	______________	______________
2. warm	______________	______________
3. proud	______________	______________
4. close	______________	______________
5. early	______________	______________

Complete each sentence with the correct comparative or superlative form of the adjective in parentheses. Write **C** if the form is comparative and **S** if it is superlative.

6. Please use the (old) ______________ of the two coins to pay the toll.

7. The clock made its (loud) ______________ ticking after midnight.

8. Dictionopolis was the (weird) ______________ name Milo had ever heard.

9. The sky tonight is (dark) ______________ than it was last night.

10. Is the Whether Man (smart) ______________ than Milo?

11. Milo knew he could find a (fast) ______________ route to Expectation than the next traveler.

12. He took the (straight) ______________ of the three roads.

Extension: Have small groups of students write a brief description of their town, something that might be included in a brochure or other promotional piece. Have students include three comparative and three superlative adjectives in their description.

Spelling Adjectives

- For adjectives ending in *e*, drop the *e* before adding *-er* or *-est*.
- For adjectives ending in a consonant and *y*, change *y* to *i* and add *-er* or *-est*.
- For one-syllable adjectives that have a single vowel before a final consonant, double the final consonant before adding *-er* or *-est*.

Complete each sentence with the correct comparative or superlative form of the adjective in parentheses.

1. The meal was much (late) ____________ than the king had hoped.

2. The deer meat tastes (salty) ____________ than the salmon.

3. I became the (sleepy) ____________ person in town when Doldrums talked.

4. The candlelight grew (dim) ____________ at the fourth hour.

5. Princess Pure Reason grew (sad) ____________ by the minute.

6. She was the (wise) ____________ person Milo met.

7. Spelling Bee was (happy) ____________ with an education than without one.

8. Is traveling by day (nice) ____________ than driving at night?

9. It was the (brave) ____________ act Milo had ever witnessed.

10. Monday seemed the (hot) ____________ day ever in the Land of Wisdom.

11. Humbug acted (grumpy) ____________ than the Lethargarian.

12. Is Princess Sweet Rhyme (young) ____________ than Princess Pure Reason?

Extension: Have students write and share a one-paragraph description of a friend or family member. Urge students to use at least three comparative and three superlative adjectives in their descriptions.

Using Comparative and Superlative Adjectives

- The **comparative** form of an adjective compares two nouns.
- The **superlative** form compares more than two nouns.
- Add *-er* or *-est* to most one-syllable and some two-syllable adjectives to form the comparative or superlative.
- For adjectives ending in *e*, drop the *e* before adding *-er* or *-est*.
- For adjectives ending in a consonant and *y*, change *y* to *i* and add *-er* or *-est*.
- For one-syllable adjectives that have a single vowel before a final consonant, double the final consonant before adding *-er* or *-est*.

Complete each sentence with the correct comparative or superlative form of the adjective in parentheses. On the line after the sentence, write the correct form of another adjective that also makes sense in the sentence.

1. Linda was the (dainty) ______________ ballerina in the troupe. ______________

2. The (fine) ______________ souvenir I found came from our vacation in Dictionopolis. ______________

3. I think that a dandelion may be a (hardy) ______________ plant than a daisy. ______________

4. "This is the (mad) ______________ person in town!" cried Milo. ______________

5. As the day grows (light) ______________, the children emerge from their cabins. ______________

6. Milo read the (large) ______________ sign on the road to Digitopolis. ______________

7. Each juggling act appeared (silly) ______________ than the last. ______________

8. Who was the (angry) ______________ of the two kings? ______________

9. After a thunderstorm, the land is (wet) ______________ than usual. ______________

10. Did you say that counting grains of sand is (easy) ______________ than naming the stars? ______________

Extension: Have students make flashcards by listing ten adjectives on index cards. Then have them work in pairs to quiz each other about the comparative and superlative forms of the adjectives.

Titles of Works

- Capitalize the first, last, and all important words in a title.
- Underline or use italics for titles of books, plays, newspapers, magazines, movies, and TV series.

Capitalize and underline the following titles as they should appear. Write the correct titles on the lines.

1. the king and i ______________________
2. martin's dictionary for kids ______________________
3. tales by phantoms ______________________
4. the digitopolis gazette ______________________

Complete the following sentences with appropriate titles.

5. My favorite funny book is called ______________________.
6. It is even funnier than ______________________.
7. Have you ordered tickets to ______________________?
8. Because my uncle likes science, he subscribes to the magazine ______________________.
9. I watch the TV series ______________________ on Saturday evenings.
10. I was really sorry when ______________________ went off the air.
11. Linda will bring ______________________ for our newspaper study on Friday.
12. How eager I am to see the movie ______________________!

Extension: Have students bring a newspaper to class. Ask them to work in groups to find titles of books, plays, newspapers, magazines, movies, and TV series.

Name ______________________________ Date ____________

TEST **Grammar** 113

Adjectives

Choose the correct replacement for the adjective form. Circle the letter of your answer.

1. The (tall) tree in the vast forest is the pine tree.
   - **a.** taller
   - **b.** tallest
   - **c.** talliest
   - **d.** tallier

2. The ride to Dictionopolis may be the (wild) ride Milo ever takes.
   - **a.** wilder
   - **b.** wildder
   - **c.** wildest
   - **d.** wildliest

3. Milo arrived (early) at the palace than at Digitopolis.
   - **a.** earlyer
   - **b.** earliest
   - **c.** earlyyer
   - **d.** earlier

4. Between Rhyme and Reason, Rhyme was (glad) that the problem was solved.
   - **a.** gladdest
   - **b.** gladder
   - **c.** gladiest
   - **d.** gladier

Circle the letter of the correction that should be made to the following sentences:

5. He was the cruelest demon of the two.
   - **a.** Change *demon* to *demons.*
   - **b.** Change *cruelest* to *crueler.*
   - **c.** Change *cruelest* to *most cruelest.*
   - **d.** Change *two* to *three.*

6. Rhyme and Reason may be the wiser of all people in Dictionopolis.
   - **a.** Change *wiser* to *wisest.*
   - **b.** Change *wiser* to *more wiser.*
   - **c.** Change *Rhyme and Reason* to *She.*
   - **d.** Change *all people* to *everyone.*

Writing Adjectives and Titles of Works

- The comparative form of an adjective compares two nouns.
- The superlative form compares more than two nouns.
- Add *-er* or *-est* to most one-syllable and some two-syllable adjectives to form the comparative or superlative.
- For adjectives ending in *e,* drop the *e* before adding *-er* or *-est.*
- For adjectives ending in a consonant and *y*, change *y* to *i* and add *-er* or *-est.*
- For one-syllable adjectives that have a single vowel before a final consonant, double the final consonant before adding *-er* or *-est.*

Mechanics

- Capitalize the first, last, and all important words in a title.
- Underline or use italics for titles of books, plays, newspapers, magazines, movies, and TV series.

Rewrite the sentences that describe each of the following pictures. Use the correct comparative or superlative form of the adjective. Write the titles.

1. Melinda reads faster of all when she sits outside.

____

2. She is fascinated by her book, the phantom tollbooth.

____

3. Marcus reads the daily herald every morning.

____

4. It arrives earliest than the other newspaper, the lincoln gazette.

____

Comparing With *More* and *Most*

- For most adjectives with two or more syllables, use *more* to form the comparative.
- For most adjectives with two or more syllables, use *most* to form the superlative.

Complete each sentence with the correct form of *more* or *most*.

1. The *Titanic* was perhaps the ____________ luxurious ocean liner of its day.

2. Do you find the green stateroom ____________ appealing than the blue one?

3. The ballroom appeared ____________ glamorous in the evening than in the day.

4. "You have been the ____________ appreciative audience of all!" exclaimed Captain Smith.

5. Of all the children on board, Monique was the ____________ mischievous.

Underline the word or words in parentheses that form a correct comparative or superlative adjective.

6. Who was the (more, most) talkative passenger on the crowded deck?

7. This winter was the (coldest, most cold) winter in the last ten years.

8. The trumpet player was (entertainier, more entertaining) than the drummer.

9. Of all the movies we viewed, Monday's comedy film was the (enjoyabelist, most enjoyable).

10. In an emergency, be sure to go to the (nearest, most near) exit.

Extension: Have students write a journal entry comparing two real or make-believe modes of transportation. Have them include three comparative and three superlative adjectives.

Name ______________________ Date ____________

Using *More* and *Most*

- Never use *more* or *most* with the *-er* or *-est* form of an adjective.

Write the comparative or superlative adjective that correctly completes each sentence.

1. "Exploring the *Titanic*" is the (most amazing, amazingest) story.

   ____

2. The ship's bow was (more deeper, deeper) than the crew thought.

   ____

3. The water appeared (more glassier, glassier) at night. ______________
4. The anchors were the (biggest, most biggest) I have ever seen.

   ____

5. The travelers strolled on the (attractivest, most attractive) decks.

   ____

6. Today's weather is (more pleasant, pleasanter) than usual. ______________
7. I grew (lazier, more lazier) the longer I sat in the deck chair. ______________
8. (Expensiver, More expensive) rooms were available in the upper decks. ______________
9. Perhaps no passengers were (eagerer, more eager) to reach the United States than the immigrants in steerage. ______________
10. Of the hundreds of passengers on the *Titanic*, I wonder who was (most unsuspecting, unsuspectingest) of the coming disaster? ______________

Extension: Have students review the sentences on this page and circle the comparative adjectives.

Finding *More* and *Most*

- For most adjectives with two or more syllables, use *more* to form the comparative.
- For most adjectives with two or more syllables, use *most* to form the superlative.
- Never use *more* or *most* with the *-er* or *-est* form of an adjective.

Write the form of the adjective in parentheses that completes the sentence correctly.

1. Our sub sank to the (low) depths possible. ______________

2. The glass dome was the (beautiful) the young girl had seen. ______________

3. We ate (elegant) food than we had thought would be served. ______________

4. The (energetic) passengers at our table danced all night. ______________

5. With each passing hour, the *Titanic* was (near) to its doom. ______________

Write the comparative or superlative adjective from each sentence in the provided space. Then write **C** if the adjective used is comparative or **S** if the adjective used is superlative.

6. "It's the most amusing puppet show I've ever attended," cried the boy. ______________

7. The divers realized that their time was becoming more precious each minute.

____

8. The air seemed freshest in the captain's cabin. ______________

9. Sailors became more frightened as the ship's bell clanged. ______________

____

10. Passengers, too, felt more panicky as news about the iceberg spread.

____

Extension: Ask students to choose a topic that interests them. Have them write five sentences using *more* and five sentences using *most*.

Hyphens

- Use a hyphen to show the division of a word at the end of a line. Divide the word between syllables.
- Use a hyphen in numbers from twenty-one through ninety-nine and in some other compound words.

Rewrite each word, using hyphens between syllables. Check your work in a dictionary, if necessary.

1. exploring ______________
2. Titanic ______________
3. introduce ______________
4. luxury ______________
5. homework ______________
6. carpet ______________
7. English ______________
8. popcorn ______________
9. cable ______________
10. marble ______________
11. fantastic ______________
12. patriot ______________
13. happiness ______________
14. validate ______________
15. total ______________
16. barnyard ______________

Use hyphens to write each number as words.

17. #39 ______________
18. #22 ______________
19. #77 ______________
20. #51 ______________
21. #86 ______________
22. #45 ______________
23. #68 ______________
24. #99 ______________

Extension: Have students write six lines about the Titanic. Have them hyphenate a word at the end of each line. Challenge them to also include at least three hyphenated numbers.

Name ______________________________ Date ____________ TEST **Grammar** 119

More* and *Most

Circle the word or words that form a comparative or superlative adjective. Write a **C** if the adjective used is comparative. Write an **S** if the adjective used is superlative.

1. It is more appropriate to call the captain "Sir" than "Mr." _____

2. The most brilliant sunsets are at sea. _____

3. The winds were calmer in the morning than the evening. _____

4. Jorge was the friendliest man at the table. _____

Choose the comparative or superlative form of the adjective in parentheses that correctly completes the sentence. Write your answer on the line provided.

5. The (short) ______________ speech of the evening was happily given by the third speaker.

6. A lifeboat is (helpful) ______________ than a life jacket.

7. The (sentimental) ________________ card she received was from her close friend Alan.

8. The more the clown blew, the (full) ______________ his balloon got.

Using *More, Most,* and Hyphens

- For most adjectives with two or more syllables, use *more* to form the comparative.
- For most adjectives with two or more syllables, use *most* to form the superlative.
- Never use *more* or *most* with the *-er* or *-est* form of an adjective.

Mechanics

- Use a hyphen to show the division of a word at the end of a line. Divide the word between syllables.
- Use a hyphen in numbers from twenty-one through ninety-nine and in some other compound words.

Rewrite each sentence using two lines. Separate the sentence between the syllables in the underlined word.

1. The luxury liner's cruise to America <u>began</u> early in the morning.

____

____

2. The ship from the <u>Caribbean</u> took the people far out to sea.

____

____

3. The children laughed at the playful <u>dolphins</u> swimming in the ocean.

____

____

Write the forms of the adjectives and numbers in parentheses that correctly complete each sentence.

4. The comedian was (humorous) ________________ than (21) ________________ clowns.

5. The (32) ________________ whales are (interesting) ________________ to watch than the (48) ________________ barracuda.

6. This fishing pole is the (practical) ________________ one we have.

Comparing with *Good*

- The comparative form of *good* is *better.*
- The superlative form of *good* is *best.*

Rewrite each sentence, using the correct comparative or superlative form of the adjective in parentheses.

1. The rocket launch was the (goodest, best) I have ever witnessed.

____

2. Scientists will get a (gooder, better) view with telescopes stationed on the moon.

____

3. The Prospector was a (better, gooder) rocket for the job.

____

4. Of the three stories, "Back to the Moon" will make the (goodest, best) movie.

____

5. The astronauts had a (better, gooder) view from the cabin.

____

6. The (goodest, best) moon rock weighed five pounds.

____

Circle the comparative or superlative form of the adjective in each sentence. In the blank, write a C if it is comparative or an S if it is superlative.

7. Did the U.S. or the Soviet Union have a better flight program? ______

8. The forward camera took the best pictures of the five developed. ______

9. The best evidence shows water ice at the lunar poles. ______

10. Scientists got better results with solar cells. ______

Extension: Have students write a paragraph comparing two or more school subjects. Have them use the comparative and superlative form of good in their comparisons.

Comparing with *Bad*

- The comparative form of *bad* is *worse.*
- The superlative form of *bad* is *worst.*

On the blank provided, write the correct comparative or superlative form of the adjective in parentheses.

____________ 1. One astronaut's meal was (badder, worse) than his partner's.

____________ 2. A Soviet crew member's living conditions are no (worser, worse) than an American astronaut's.

____________ 3. One of the lunar scientists was the (baddest, worst) math student in his sixth-grade class.

____________ 4. Which is (worse, badder), losing equipment or breaking a tool?

____________ 5. The temperature readings were the (baddest, worst) after dark.

____________ 6. This is the (baddest, worst) computer on the space shuttle.

____________ 7. Pictures taken from Earth are (worse, worst) than pictures taken on the moon.

____________ 8. Which of the three assignments is the (worse, worst)?

____________ 9. This space meal is (worse, worst) than the one we had this morning.

____________ 10. My space sickness is (worse, worst) today than it was yesterday.

Extension: Have students work in pairs to write a paragraph comparing two or more pollution problems. Have them use the comparative and superlative forms of *bad* in their comparisons.

Comparing with *Good* and *Bad*

Comparing with *Good*
- The comparative form of *good* is *better.*
- The superlative form of *good* is *best.*

Comparing with *Bad*
- The comparative form of *bad* is *worse.*
- The superlative form of *bad* is *worst.*

Rewrite each sentence using the correct comparative or superlative form of the adjective in parentheses.

1. Sue is a (good) chess player than Chris.

____

2. Clear skies are the (good) conditions for a shuttle launch.

____

3. Tasteless space food makes my hunger grow (bad).

____

4. Space travel will give us a (good) understanding of our universe.

____

5. Some space travelers have a (bad) time sleeping in space than at home.

____

6. Astronauts train to handle the (bad) events that can occur in flight.

____

7. Many astronauts have reported that the (good) view of Earth is from space.

____

8. Usually, even the (bad) moon walker can travel faster with practice.

____

9. The television reporter said that the transmission was getting (good).

____

10. The sunspot activity has been (bad) than usual.

____

Extension: Have students circle the superlative form of the adjectives in the above sentences.

Quotations

- Use quotation marks before and after the words of a direct quotation.
- Use a comma before a quotation when the speaker's name comes first.
- Use a comma, a question mark, or an exclamation point to end the quotation when the speaker's name comes last.

Proofread each sentence. Then rewrite the sentence using the correct punctuation.

1. Look at the stars exclaimed Tamika

____

2. Bill asked Do you think there's life on Mars

____

3. Would you like a career in the space industry asked the teacher

____

4. The student replied I'd have to really study my math first

____

5. I'd love to spend a vacation on the moon said Maria.

____

6. Me too yelled Jake

____

7. Tom asked Will ordinary citizens fly to other planets in the future

____

8. A trip into outer space would be too expensive for me said Courtney

____

9. I wonder if they will have regularly scheduled flights to the moon said Maria.

____

10. Do you think they will build tourist attractions there asked Jake.

____

Extension: Have students write a dialogue they might have with a Martian. Remind them to use the correct punctuation.

Name ______________________ Date ____________ TEST **Grammar** 125

Adjectives

Choose the best comparative or superlative form of *good*. Circle the letter of your choice.

1. Captain Smith's cabin was the (good) of the two.
   a. better
   b. goodest
   c. best
   d. gooder
2. The tourist said a lunar trip is (good) than a vacation to Rome.
   a. goodest
   b. gooder
   c. better
   d. best
3. The navigator chose the (good) flight path of the three he studied.
   a. better
   b. gooder
   c. best
   d. goodest
4. NASA has the (good) site for space study on the Internet.
   a. goodest
   b. best
   c. gooder
   d. better

Choose the best comparative or superlative form of *bad*. Circle the letter of your choice.

5. Space travel cannot be (bad) than flying in a helicopter.
   a. badder
   b. worse
   c. baddest
   d. worst

6. For one astronaut, lift-off is the (bad) part of the trip.
   a. worst
   b. worse
   c. baddest
   d. badder

7. Which is (bad), losing your oxygen or being exposed to heat?
   a. worst
   b. badder
   c. baddest
   d. worse

8. I can't think of a (bad) experience than being stranded in space.
   a. badder
   b. baddest
   c. worst
   d. worse

Using Adjectives and Quotations

Comparing with *Good*
- The comparative form of *good* is *better*.
- The superlative form of *good* is *best*.

Comparing with *Bad*
- The comparative form of *bad* is *worse*.
- The superlative form of *bad* is *worst*.

Mechanics

- Use quotation marks before and after the words of a direct quotation.
- Use a comma before a quotation when the speaker's name comes first.
- Use a comma, a question mark, or an exclamation point to end the quotation when the speaker's name comes last.

Choose the correct form of *good* and *bad* in each sentence. Add the correct punctuation. Then rewrite the sentence on the line provided. In the space above, draw the picture that the sentences suggest.

1. Which is the (better, goodest) vacation, golfing on the moon or sunbathing in Mexico asked Lin

____

____

2. A shy tourist will have the (best, bestest) vacation on the moon said the tour guide

____

3. Jeff cried touring the lunar surface is (bester, better) than race car driving

____

4. These moon rocks are (gooder, better) than those Egyptian coins said the archeologist

____

____

Adjectives

Read the passage and look at each underlined section. Is there a mistake? If there is, how do you correct it? Circle the letter of your answer.

Jackie's school held a Careers Day in October. <u>The best guest speaker talked about the following topics; computer technology, American history, and space exploration.</u> (1) The students listened carefully. <u>Jackie asked, "will I have to be more skilled in math if I am a computer programmer?"</u> (2) The speaker assured Jackie that he could handle the job. "Then a math class may be easier than I think," said Jackie.

1. **A.** Change *best* to *goodest.*
   B. Replace the semicolon with a colon.
   C. Change *American* to *american.*
   D. No mistake.

2. **F.** Remove the comma.
   G. Change *will* to *Will.*
   H. Change *more skilled* to *skillder.*
   J. No mistake.

Lupe and Kelly went to the movies last Saturday. <u>They arrived at 2:30 to see *"Miracle in Miss Jake's Class."*</u> (3) They bought tickets and found their seats. <u>Afterwards, Lupe thought the two-hour film was funnier than a comedy they watched the month before</u> (4). Kelly disagreed. She said, "This movie was worse than that movie."

3. **A.** Remove the quotation marks.
   B. Change *in* to *In.*
   C. Change *2:30* to *230.*
   D. No mistake.

4. **F.** Change *a* to *an.*
   G. Change *two-hour* to *two hour.*
   H. Change *funnier* to *more funny.*
   J. No mistake.

Name ______________________ Date ____________ REVIEW **Grammar** 128

Adjectives

Jeanne asked "Have you read Wilson Rawls's novel *Where the Red Fern Grows*? (5)
You'd love it. This book has everything: great plot, realistic characters, and vivid imagery. (6) Everyone should read it."

5. **A.** Add a comma after *asked.*
   B. Change *the* to *The.*
   C. Place quotation marks after *Grows.*
   D. No mistake.

6. **F.** Change *this* to *these.*
   G. Change the colon to a period.
   H. Add quotation marks after *imagery.*
   J. No mistake.

Read the sentences below. What adjective form is each underlined word? Circle the letter of your answer.

Nokalita thinks the British (7) author Rudyard Kipling is one of the best (8) authors in her literature book. She told me, "Kipling's story is creative. I recommend this story to all of my friends."

7. **A.** Proper adjective
   B. Demonstrative adjective
   C. Comparative adjective
   D. Superlative adjective

8. **F.** Demonstrative adjective
   G. Superlative adjective
   H. Comparative adjective
   J. Proper adjective

Pronouns and Antecedents

- A **pronoun** is a word that takes the place of one or more nouns and the words that go with the nouns.
- The **antecedent**, or **referent**, of a pronoun is the word or group of words to which the pronoun refers. Pronouns and antecedents must agree.

Write a pronoun to take the place of the underlined noun or noun phrase. Write your answer on the line provided.

1. Casey meets her friends at the library after school. ____________
2. Students complete their homework and check out books there. ____________
3. Barney wanted to know if Phil got Paw Paw's message. ____________
4. Today the children can walk to the park. ____________
5. Has Mike seen the zoo's snake and reptile exhibit? ____________

Write the pronoun in the parentheses that agrees with its underlined antecedent on the line provided.

6. Phil the Pill pretended (he, she) was brave in front of his mother. ____________
7. Paw Paw became anxious if (she, they) could not listen to the radio. ____________
8. Laurence Yep writes novels, and I have read some of (he, them). ____________
9. When Paw Paw talked to us, (he, she) was serious. ____________
10. Phil tried to fix the radio, but (they, it) still would not work. ____________

Extension: Write a short story about a visit Casey might take to the zoo with Paw Paw. Use ten pronouns and circle each one.

Name ______________________________ Date ____________

Singular and Plural Pronouns

- Singular pronouns are *I, you, he, she, it, me, him, her.*
- Plural pronouns are *we, you, they, us, them.*

Circle the pronoun in each of the following sentences. Write an S if the pronoun is singular. Write a P if the pronoun is plural.

1. I wonder why Phil is called Phil the Pill. ______
2. After lunchtime they attend classes in Chinese. ______
3. The family takes plenty of picnic sandwiches with them. ______
4. Will Mike and Sharon hike in the woods with us? ______
5. Chinese is an interesting language, but it is difficult to learn. ______
6. She is interested in Paw Paw's statue of Buddha. ______

Circle the pronoun in each of the following sentences. Write its antecedent.

7. Phil drove to Sacramento Street, and then he turned left. ____________
8. Casey was brought up by Barney, but she lived with Phil's family. ____________
9. The Chinese school was old, but the students loved attending it.

   ____

10. Phil and Casey reached Paw Paw's apartment door, and they rang the buzzer.

    ____

11. Paw Paw looked at Phil the Pill and asked him to leave. ____________
12. Though Paw Paw looked hard for the glasses, the grandmother could not find them.

    ____

Extension: Work in groups to write a sentence for each pronoun listed above.

Using Pronouns

- A **pronoun** is a word that takes the place of one or more nouns and the words that go with the nouns.
- The **antecedent**, or **referent**, of a pronoun is the word or group of words to which the pronoun refers. Pronouns and antecedents must agree.
- Singular pronouns are *I, you, he, she, it, me, him, her.*
- Plural pronouns are *we, you, they, us, them.*

Choose the pronoun in parentheses that correctly completes each sentence.

1. During the holidays (he, they) visit their grandmother's house. ____________

2. (We, She) takes two apple pies from the oven. ____________

3. (It, They) were happiest when Marshal Dillon spoke on the radio. ____________

4. This is (me, they) pictured in the family portrait. ____________

5. Father called Casey, and then (he, they) answered his mail. ____________

Fill in the blank with an appropriate pronoun.

6. ____________ hopes Casey enjoys living in the apartment.

7. Will ____________ watch my favorite television program with me tonight?

8. ____________ sound like interesting characters.

9. Phil was sad when he had to leave ____________ with Paw Paw.

10. She is moving and will send ____________ a letter soon.

Extension: Write a letter to Casey. Circle the pronouns that you use.

Contractions

- A contraction may be formed by combining a pronoun and a verb.
- An apostrophe shows where one or more letters have been left out.

Rewrite each of the following sentences using the contractions for the pronoun and verb in parentheses.

1. (You have) just read *Child of the Owl* by Laurence Yep.

____

2. (He has) written novels popular among young adults.

____

3. The teacher said that (they are) located in the local library.

____

4. I can lend you *The Rainbow People* since (I have) a copy at home.

____

5. (We are) going to the library after school.

____

Rewrite each of the following sentences changing the contraction in parentheses into the pronoun and verb that it represents.

6. (She'll) borrow *Dragonwings* and read it over summer break.

____

7. (It's) a novel that was named a Newbery Medal Honor Book in 1976.

____

8. Sue said, "(We've) heard Yep writes about his life as a Chinese American."

____

9. Once you read one of Yep's books, (you're) going to ask for another.

____

10. (I'm) one of his biggest fans.

____

Extension: Work with a partner to make up sentences using pronoun contractions.

Name ______________________________ Date ____________ TEST **Grammar** 133

Pronouns

Circle the pronoun in parentheses that correctly completes the following sentences.

1. Paw Paw hung lace curtains, and visitors could see through (them, it).

2. Casey read the novel and returned (it, him) to the library yesterday.

3. Phil the Pill tells Paw Paw (he, we) thinks she is kind.

4. Barney, will (you, her) E-mail your reply tomorrow?

5. Casey likes pie, so (she, it) asks for some.

Circle the pronoun in each of the following sentences. Write the pronoun's antecedent on the line provided.

6. Casey is going to the mall, and Barney will go with her. ____________

7. Phil wrote a name on the letter to sign it. ____________

8. The granddaughter likes the carrots and will eat them. ____________

9. Yep's vivid words help us, the readers, picture Paw Paw's house.

   ____

10. Mario and Chen saw the movie, but they did not care for the acting.

    ____

Pronouns and Contractions

- A **pronoun** is a word that takes the place of one or more nouns and the words that go with the nouns.
- The **antecedent**, or **referent**, of a pronoun is the word or group of words to which the pronoun refers. Pronouns and antecedents must agree.
- Singular pronouns are *I, you, he, she, it, me, him, her.*
- Plural pronouns are *we, you, they, us, them.*

Mechanics

- A contraction may be formed by combining a pronoun and a verb.
- An apostrophe shows where one or more letters have been left out.

Read the sentences about the picture. Each sentence contains a mistake. Rewrite each sentence correctly.

1. This cable car runs every day, and they is a popular tourist attraction.

____

2. Its a lot of fun to ride on a cable car.

____

3. Ive always enjoyed visiting San Francisco.

____

4. Mom uses the cable car when he shops in Union Square.

____

5. My uncle strolls up Nob Hill when they wants some exercise.

____

6. Youd enjoy visiting Coit Tower and Fisherman's Wharf.

____

Subject Pronouns

- A **subject pronoun** is used as the subject of a sentence.
- Use a subject pronoun when the pronoun is part of a compound subject.
- *I, you, he, she, it, we,* and *they* are subject pronouns.

Choose the correct pronoun in parentheses to correctly complete each sentence.

1. The king and (I, me) ____________ were tired of listening to the queen.

2. (He, Him) ____________ agreed to fight the ferocious monster.

3. All of the villagers and (she, her) ____________ feared the Chimera.

4. (They, Them) ____________ advised Bellerophon to take the crooked path through the woods.

Read each sentence and circle any incorrect pronoun. Rewrite each sentence correctly on the line provided. If the pronoun is correct, write Correct instead of the sentence.

5. Me will ride Pegasus into the sky.

____

6. Them plan to deal with the creature.

____

7. The beautiful woman and him stared at the winged horse.

____

8. You and it will reach the kingdom of Argos by nightfall.

____

9. Pegasus and him circled the town and swooped back to earth.

____

10. Us came to a farming village that lay in ruins.

____

Extension: Work with a partner to write a new ending for Bellerophon. Include and circle five subject pronouns in your work.

Object Pronouns

- An **object pronoun** is used as the object of a verb or as the object of a preposition, such as *for, at, with,* or *to.*
- Use an object pronoun when the pronoun is part of a compound object.
- *Me, you, him, her, it, us,* and *them* are object pronouns.

Circle the incorrect pronoun, and write the correct pronoun in the blank provided.

1. The king begged they to destroy the Chimera. ____________

2. Bellerophon carried the horse's bridle to she. ____________

3. Please take the king's message to Pegasus and he. ____________

4. Will the miller inspect the wheat field with the farmer and I? ____________

5. The Chimera attacked the villagers and brought they great unhappiness.

____

Circle the object pronoun in parentheses that correctly completes each sentence.

6. The shop keeper cried out, "Stop!" to Bellerophon and (he, him).

7. The horses grazed idly by the pond and ignored (it, I).

8. The soldiers exclaimed, "We will follow our king and (she, her)!"

9. Bellerophon asked (they, them), "Please direct me to the nearest village."

10. Will you accompany the king and (we, us) to the forest?

Extension: Write a letter of complaint to the Chimera. Include five object pronouns.

Finding Subject and Object Pronouns

- A **subject pronoun** is used as the subject of a sentence.
- Use a subject pronoun when the pronoun is part of a compound subject.
- *I, you, he, she, it, we,* and *they* are subject pronouns.
- An **object pronoun** is used as the object of a verb or as the object of a preposition, such as *for, at, with,* or *to.*
- Use an object pronoun when the pronoun is part of a compound object.
- *Me, you, him, her, it, us,* and *them* are object pronouns.

Circle the pronouns in each of the following sentences. Write an **S** if the pronoun is a subject pronoun. Write an **O** if the pronoun is an object pronoun.

1. The king's soldiers and he failed to tame the monster. ____________

2. Do you and the other children want a ride in the hay cart? ____________

3. Margaret grew tired of planting them in the garden. ____________

4. The brave prince and I are off to capture the Chimera. ____________

5. The hungry chickens scurried to it. ____________

Write an appropriate pronoun on the blank provided. Do not use the same pronoun twice.

6. Bellerophon and ____________ tried to pet the winged horse.

7. The town's mayor wrote letters to the queen and ____________.

8. ____________ agreed to buy the bridles for the horses.

9. Can ____________ hit the target with the arrow?

10. The townspeople heard a thunderous roar from ____________.

Extension: Write five sentences. Include a subject and an object pronoun in each sentence.

Using *I* and *Me*

- Always write the pronoun *I* with a capital letter.
- Use *I* or *me* last when talking about yourself and another person.

Rewrite each sentence correctly.

1. Pegasus came to live with me and my family last summer.

____

2. I and my brother were surprised that a winged horse really exists.

____

3. He relies on me and Bob to feed and water him.

____

4. After lunch Katy and i are going to take a ride on Pegasus.

____

5. Will i and my father buy Pegasus a colorful saddle?

____

6. Everyone in town knows about me and my horse.

____

7. Pegasus and i appeared on a national TV talk show.

____

8. Now people across the nation send me and Pegasus fan mail.

____

9. Pegasus doesn't write, so i have to answer the mail.

____

10. I and he do not really enjoy being famous.

____

Extension: Write a description of the ideal pet. Use *I* and *me* three times each in your work.

Pronouns

Read the first sentence of each set. One of the four sentences that follows correctly replaces the underlined subject with a subject pronoun. Circle the letter of the correct sentence.

1. <u>The flying horse Pegasus</u> transported the prince across the kingdom.
   - **a.** He transported the prince across the kingdom.
   - **b.** They transported the prince across the kingdom.
   - **c.** Pegasus transported him across the kingdom.
   - **d.** The flying horse Pegasus transported them across the kingdom.

2. <u>Many young men</u> have tried to slay the Chimera.
   - **a.** He have tried to slay the Chimera.
   - **b.** They have tried to slay the Chimera.
   - **c.** Young men have tried to slay the Chimera.
   - **d.** Many young men have tried to slay the Chimera.

3. <u>Bellerophon and Pegasus</u> searched for the wicked creature and its trail.
   - **a.** Bellerophon and Pegasus searched for them.
   - **b.** He searched for the wicked creature and its trail.
   - **c.** They searched for the wicked creature and its trail.
   - **d.** Bellerophon and Pegasus searched for him and its trail.

Read the first sentence of each set. One of the four sentences that follows correctly replaces the underlined object with an object pronoun. Circle the letter of the correct sentence.

4. The king advised <u>Bellerophon</u> to take the crooked path through the woods.
   - **a.** The king advised them to take the crooked path through the woods.
   - **b.** The king advised he to take the crooked path through the woods.
   - **c.** The king advised him to take the crooked path through the woods.
   - **d.** The king advised us to take the crooked path through the woods.

5. The ancient pot shows <u>Athena</u> with a battle shield.
   - **a.** They show Athena with a battle shield.
   - **b.** The ancient pot shows her with a battle shield.
   - **c.** The pot shows them with a battle shield.
   - **d.** It shows Athena with them.

Subject and Object Pronouns

- A **subject pronoun** is used as the subject of a sentence.
- Use a subject pronoun when the pronoun is part of a compound subject.
- *I, you, he, she, it, we,* and *they* are subject pronouns.
- An **object pronoun** is used as the object of a verb or as the object of a preposition, such as *for, at, with,* or *to.*
- Use an object pronoun when the pronoun is part of a compound object.
- *Me, you, him, her, it, us,* and *them* are object pronouns.

Mechanics

- Always write the pronoun *I* with a capital letter.
- Use *I* or *me* when talking about yourself and another person.

Read each sentence aloud. Circle the subject or object pronoun in parentheses that correctly completes each sentence.

1. My brother and (she, her) wish they owned a horse.

2. Raising a pet is important to you and (we, us).

3. "You would have to take proper care of (him, he)," said Mother.

4. Will you buy the grain and horse feed from (they, them)?

5. (Us, We) brush the horse until his coat shines.

Read each sentence aloud. Rewrite each sentence correctly.

6. My brother and i feed the horse every morning.

____

7. Of course i and my sister ride the horse after school each day.

____

8. Do you want to come for a ride with me and my horse?

____

Possessive Pronouns

- A **possessive pronoun** takes the place of a possessive noun. It shows *who* or *what* owns something.
- Some possessive pronouns are used before nouns (*my, your, his, her, its, our, your, their.*)

Write the possessive pronouns in the following sentences on the line provided.

1. Please point to your destination on the lunar map. __________
2. The robot turned its mechanical arm toward the telescope. __________
3. Commander Covey was inspired by their successful mission. __________
4. Without spacesuits our bodies are unprotected from the sun's heat. __________
5. Jeff and Story prepared the space shuttle for my flight. __________
6. "Is her tether tied properly?" asked the crew member. __________
7. Roberto will study astronomy in his science class next year. __________

Replace the underlined word or words with a possessive pronoun.

8. Claude heard <u>Kathy's</u> voice over the radio. __________
9. <u>NASA's</u> goal was to land the first man on the moon. __________
10. When Covey took control, <u>the Commander's</u> thoughts turned toward the Hubble. __________
11. <u>The crew's</u> power tools failed to work on the jammed door. __________
12. Learn more about <u>the mission's</u> history on the NASA Web site. __________

Extension: Make a list of five possessive nouns. Exchange your list with a partner and write possessive pronouns for each possessive noun.

Locating Possessive Pronouns

- Some possessive pronouns can stand alone (*mine, yours, his, hers, its, ours, yours, theirs.*)
- Do not confuse the pronouns *its, your, their, and theirs* with the contractions *it's, you're, they're,* and *there's.*

Find the possessive pronoun in each of the following sentences.

1. The tools to install the solar arrays were ours. ____________

2. Jeff saw a pair of space gloves, but they were not his. ____________

3. The job of fixing the panel was hers. ____________

4. The battery pack and lunar maps are theirs. ____________

5. "The computer disk is mine," replied Covey. ____________

Circle the pronoun in parentheses that correctly completes each sentence.

6. Is the camera film (you'res, yours)?

7. Is the battery pack (you'res, yours)?

8. I believe it is (theirs, there's).

9. (It's, Its) tiny screw was loose.

10. The tether is stored in (its, it's) compartment.

11. (There's, Theirs) is the best view of Earth.

12. (My, Mine) is the space suit with the blue band.

Extension: Write a letter to Commander Covey explaining your interest in space travel. Include ten possessive pronouns. Exchange letters with a partner and circle the possessive pronouns.

Reviewing Pronouns

- A **possessive pronoun** takes the place of a possessive noun. It shows *who* or *what* owns something.
- Some possessive pronouns are used before nouns (*my, your, his, her, its, our, your, their.*)
- Some possessive pronouns can stand alone (*mine, yours, his, hers, its, ours, yours, theirs.*)
- Do not confuse the pronouns *its, your, their,* and *theirs* with the contractions *it's, you're, they're,* and *there's.*

Read each sentence. If the underlined possessive pronoun is incorrect, write the correct pronoun on the line provided. If the pronoun is correct, write **C**.

1. Mine friend Komiko invited me to watch the space launch with her. __________

2. The space museum supported the astronauts and told their story. __________

3. Do you have a special place to set up you're telescope? __________

4. The story tells about a space shuttle and it's mission. __________

5. Covey asked, "Are the math calculations there's or NASA's?" __________

Write an appropriate possessive pronoun on the blank provided. Do not use the same pronoun twice.

6. __________ estimated time of arrival is 2:45 A.M.

7. Claude recorded his thoughts in __________ journal every night.

8. The flight schedule and the calculator are __________ materials.

9. The Smithsonian Institute's moon rocks are preserved in __________ museum.

10. You can borrow __________ star chart, but please return it.

Extension: Write a conversation between two astronauts. Use and circle ten possessive pronouns.

Name ______________________ Date ____________

Contractions and Possessives

- An apostrophe takes the place of letters left out of a contraction.
- Possessive pronouns do not have apostrophes. Do not confuse possessive pronouns with contractions.

Choose the pronoun or contraction that correctly completes each sentence. Write the sentence on the lines provided.

1. The NASA scientists calculated (their, they're) arrival.

____

2. The astronaut found (it's, its) matching glove in the suit pocket.

____

3. (There's, Theirs) are the blue helmets.

____

4. (Your, You're) view of Earth is spectacular.

____

5. (Their, They're) calculations were correct.

____

6. I'm sure (you're, your) plans for the landing will be successful.

____

7. (Its, It's) a perfect day for the space shuttle's liftoff.

____

8. Reporters claimed the stories were (there's, theirs).

____

9. (They're, Their) eager to return to space.

____

10. (You're, Your) the best person for this space mission.

____

Extension: Write a five sentence test using sentences like the ones above. Provide the answers.

Name ______________________ Date ____________ TEST **Grammar** 145

Pronouns

Circle the correct possessive pronoun or contraction in parentheses. Write the sentence correctly on the line provided.

1. "Was (your, you're) ride on the robot arm fun?" asked Tom.

____

2. Kathy and (her, hers) partner worked on the spacecraft.

____

3. "Do you have (mine, my) flight helmet?" asked the cook.

____

4. I don't want to eat the dessert if (it's, its) yours.

____

5. The space crew reacted to (their, they're) news with enthusiasm.

____

6. (It's, Its) mechanical arm reached for the lunar rock.

____

7. The repair kit for the Hubble is (our, ours).

____

8. The responsibility to repair the *Endeavour* was (my, mine).

____

9. Credit for the successful repair was (him, his).

____

10. (Her, Hers) trip to space was exciting.

____

/10

Possessive Pronouns and Contractions

- A **possessive pronoun** takes the place of a possessive noun. It shows who or what owns something.
- Some possessive pronouns are used before nouns (*my, your, his, her, its, our, your, their*).
- Some possessive pronouns can stand alone (*mine, yours, his, hers, its, ours, yours, theirs*).
- Do not confuse the pronouns *its, your, their,* and *theirs* with the contractions *it's, you're, they're,* and *there's*.

Mechanics

- An apostrophe takes the place of letters left out of a contraction.
- Possessive pronouns do not have apostrophes. Do not confuse possessive pronouns with contractions.

Read the sentences about the picture. Circle the possessive pronoun in parentheses that correctly completes each sentence. Rewrite each sentence.

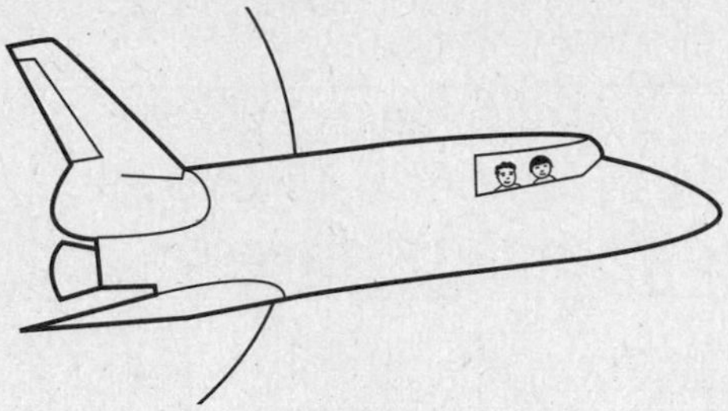

1. (My, Mine) greatest desire is to travel in space.

____

2. (They're, Their) goal is to become the first students to land on the moon.

____

3. They are awestruck with the moon and (it's, its) lunar mountains.

____

4. When the students return from the mission, the fame will be (theirs, there's).

____

5. "We are waiting for (your, you're) E-mail," joked Mission Control.

____

Indefinite Pronouns and Singular Verbs

- An **indefinite pronoun** does not refer to a particular person, place, or thing.
- Use a singular verb with a singular indefinite pronoun, such as *anybody, anyone, anything, each, everybody, everyone, everything, nobody, nothing, somebody, someone, something.*

Read each sentence. Circle the verb in parentheses that correctly completes the sentence.

1. Everybody (is, are) convinced Rumpelstiltskin's daughter can spin straw into gold.
2. Unfortunately, each of the stories (were, was) false.
3. Everything (need, needs) to be cleaned up by the end of the day.
4. Somebody (deliver, delivers) hay to the castle's front gate.
5. If anyone (ask, asks) you to swim in the moat, say no.

Change the singular or plural verb in each sentence so that it agrees with the indefinite pronoun. Write the sentence.

6. Somebody must helps the poor farmers with their wheat fields.

____

7. Everyone agree that Rumpelstiltskin's daughter should help the hungry children.

____

8. No one are more disappointed with the outcome than the king.

____

9. Nothing seem too difficult for her.

____

10. Everybody respect her kindness.

____

Extension: Find and underline singular indefinite pronouns in a newspaper article you bring to class.

Indefinite Pronouns and Plural Verbs

- Use a plural verb with a plural indefinite pronoun, such as *both, few, many, others, several.*

Circle the verb in parentheses that correctly completes the sentence.

1. Many of us (enjoys, enjoy) fairy tales about evil kings.

2. A few (reads, read) stories every night.

3. Both of them (wishes, wish) to marry Meredith.

4. Several (begs, beg) Rumpelstiltskin's daughter to talk to the king.

5. Others (likes, like) to eat the roasted corn.

Circle the indefinite pronoun. Write S if the indefinite pronoun is singular. Write P if it is plural.

6. A few of the coins were buried in the ground. ____

7. Others were scattered on top of the soil. ____

8. Somebody traveled the kingdom spreading the story of Rumpelstiltskin. ____

9. The daughter said there was something better than gold. ____

10. Have many seen the glittering coach with two guards? ____

Extension: Write five sentences using plural indefinite pronouns.

Working With Indefinite Pronouns

- An **indefinite pronoun** does not refer to a particular person, place, or thing.
- Use a singular verb with a singular indefinite pronoun, such as *anybody, anyone, anything, each, everybody, everyone, everything, nobody, nothing, somebody, someone, something.*
- Use a plural verb with a plural indefinite pronoun, such as *both, few, many, others, several.*

Circle the indefinite pronoun that correctly completes the sentence.

1. (Everybody, Both) carry baskets of wheat and barley.

2. (Several, Each) of the children looks healthy and content.

3. (Everything, Others) grows quickly in her vegetable garden.

4. (Few, Nobody) is allowed to rest until the king is satisfied.

5. (Many, Someone) in the kingdom sells pottery to the farmers.

Fill in the blank with an appropriate indefinite pronoun. Do not use a pronoun more than once.

6. ____________ is more desirable to the king than gold.

7. ____________ of the children race through the dark and spooky forest.

8. ____________ ride horses down the crooked lane to the village.

9. ____________ loves Rumpelstiltskin's daughter for saving the land.

10. ____________ walk to the palace to pay their taxes.

Extension: Write a letter to Rumpelstiltskin's daughter in which you complain about how the king's policies keep the people in poverty. Use five indefinite pronouns.

Quotations

- Use quotation marks before and after the words of a direct quotation.
- Begin a quotation with a capital letter.
- Begin a new paragraph and use a separate set of quotation marks when the speaker changes in dialogue.

Form paragraphs out of the following sentences. Use the proper quotation marks and capital letters in each sentence.

The miller said my daughter is so talented she can spin gold. One villager said nobody can turn regular hay into something as precious as gold. The miller replied the king thinks she can, and that is all that matters. She is with him at this very moment. However, the villager was still doubtful and said you'll have to show me first. If it's true, we can all be rich.

____

____

____

____

____

____

____

Extension: Work with a partner to write a dialogue between a villager and the king. Use the correct punctuation and paragraph structure for quotations.

Pronouns

Read the first sentence of each set. One of the four sentences that follows corrects the agreement between an indefinite pronoun and its verb. Circle the letter of the correct sentence.

1. Each of the cows wander off.
   - **a.** Change wander to wanders.
   - **b.** Change Each to Every.
   - **c.** Change Each to All.
   - **d.** Change Each to Few.

2. Somebody like to ride through a dark forest.
   - **a.** Change Somebody to Everyone.
   - **b.** Change Somebody to Few.
   - **c.** Change Somebody to Each.
   - **d.** Change Somebody to Nobody.

3. Everything in the class reminds students that someone love to read fairy tales.
   - **a.** Change Everything to Nothing.
   - **b.** Change reminds to remind.
   - **c.** Change someone to nobody.
   - **d.** Change love to loves.

Circle the letter that best answers each of the following questions.

4. Which of the following statements about indefinite pronouns is true?
   - **a.** Indefinite pronouns, such as *both*, use a singular verb.
   - **b.** Indefinite pronouns take the place of certain people, places, and things.
   - **c.** Indefinite pronouns, such as *each*, use a plural verb.
   - **d.** Indefinite pronouns do not refer to a particular person, place, or thing.

5. Which of the following sentences contains an indefinite pronoun?
   - **a.** My flowers scattered in the wind.
   - **b.** Several pass by the church.
   - **c.** The spinning wheel is hers.
   - **d.** She spun gold out of hay.

Practicing With Indefinite Pronouns and Quotations

- An **indefinite pronoun** does not refer to a particular person, place, or thing.
- Use a singular verb with a singular indefinite pronoun, such as *anybody, anyone, anything, each, everybody, everyone, everything, nobody, nothing, somebody, someone, something*.
- Use a plural verb with a plural indefinite pronoun, such as *both, few, many, others, several.*

Mechanics

- Use quotation marks before and after the words of a direct quotation.
- Begin a quotation with a capital letter.
- Begin a new paragraph and use a separate set of quotation marks when the speaker changes in dialogue.

Read the following dialogue between the king and Rumpelstiltskin's daughter aloud to a partner. Then choose the verb that correctly completes each sentence. Rewrite the dialogue, using the proper quotation marks and capital letters.

Rumpelstiltskin's daughter said nobody (like, likes) a stingy king. Everyone (love, loves) me said the ruler. Many cannot (afford, affords) to feed their children when taxes are so high said the girl. The king replied times are not hard and everyone (acts, act) happy. Few (risks, risk) making their king unhappy by complaining she said.

____

____

____

____

____

Pronoun-Verb Agreement

- A verb must agree with its subject pronoun.

Pronouns	**Verbs**
He, she, it	walks, is, was, has
We, you, they	walk, are, were, have
I	walk, am, was, have

Circle the verb in parentheses that correctly completes each sentence. Rewrite the sentence.

1. He (barters, barter) with the merchant for bread and corn.

____

2. It (is, are) easy to get money from ATM machines.

____

3. Juan and I (shop, shops) for vegetables at the bazaar.

____

4. (Were, Was) you satisfied with the restaurant's service?

____

5. She (pays, pay) for her clothes with credit cards.

____

Circle the subject pronoun that correctly completes each sentence. Rewrite the sentence.

6. (We, He) count the metal coins carefully.

____

7. (They, She) pay the hired workers with shells.

____

8. (He, We) have rare coins from around the world.

____

9. In Egypt (I, she) uses precious metals for money.

____

10. (It, You) is wise to save your money.

____

Extension: Draw an arrow from the subject pronoun to the verb with which it agrees.

Indefinite Pronouns and Verbs

Verbs must also agree with indefinite pronouns.

- Use a singular verb with a singular indefinite pronoun.
- Use a plural verb with a plural indefinite pronoun.

Rewrite each sentence, choosing the verb in parentheses that agrees with the indefinite pronoun.

1. Everything (is, are) too expensive for the poor farmers.

____

2. No one (trade, trades) in beads at today's shopping mall.

____

3. Both of the banks (offer, offers) savings accounts.

____

4. A few of the dollar bills (are, is) old.

____

5. Nothing (costs, cost) over five shells in that shop.

____

6. Others (require, requires) borrowers to pay interest.

____

7. Everyone (learn, learns) that the Chinese invented paper money.

____

8. (Do, Does) anybody want to barter for lunch?

____

9. Many (have, has) piggy banks for their extra change.

____

10. Several (participate, participates) in the auction.

____

Extension: Underline each indefinite pronoun above and label whether each is singular or plural.

Reviewing Pronouns and Verbs

- A verb must agree with its subject pronoun.

Pronouns	Verbs
He, she, it	walks, is, was, has
We, you, they	walk, are, were, have
I	walk, am, was, have

Change each verb in the following sentences so that it agrees with the subject pronoun. Write your response on the line provided.

1. Nobody need money if they can barter for their goods. ____________
2. Nothing bother me more than losing my money in the store. ____________
3. She take shells, seeds, and tea leaves to the village. ____________
4. I trades my camel for enough gold to pay for my trip to Morocco. ____________
5. Everyone use wampum made of little shells and beads. ____________

Fill in the blank with a pronoun that agrees with the verb. Do not use the same pronoun more than once.

6. ____________ brings cowrie shells from Africa to barter for wheat.
7. ____________ buy coins from Persia, Rome, and Egypt.
8. His brother and ____________ trade a shekel for corn.
9. ____________ barter their sandwiches for fruit at lunchtime.
10. ____________ and ____________ deposit our savings at the local bank.

Extension: Write five sentences about food bartering at lunchtime. Use a different pronoun in each sentence.

Titles of Works

- Underline or use italics for titles of books, plays, newspapers, magazines, movies, and TV series.
- Put quotation marks around titles of poems, short stories, essays, songs, articles, and book chapters.

Rewrite each sentence correctly. Underline or use quotation marks on the titles.

1. Have you read the book The Art of Bartering by Joseph Hill?

____

2. We read the short story Gold and Silver in class yesterday.

____

3. My father subscribes to Coin Collecting.

____

4. Read the newspaper The New York Times to learn about trading today.

____

5. Linda looks for an article called Bartering with Your Peanut Butter Sandwich.

____

6. Margaret plans to see the movie The Stockbroker and the Trader.

____

7. Kurt's essay was called My Current Savings Account.

____

8. I just heard the new song Money.

____

9. My mother is reading a book titled Investing for the Future.

____

10. My sister wrote an article called Planning Your Portfolio.

____

Extension: Write six sentences using titles. Use three titles requiring quotation marks and three that should be underlined.

Pronouns

Write the verb in parentheses that correctly completes each sentence.

1. Everyone (wait, waits) quietly for the historian to speak. ____________

2. We (study, studies) interesting tales about ancient Persia. ____________

3. Jason and she (trade, trades) coins with the shopkeeper. ____________

4. He (prefer, prefers) to collect stamps instead of coins. ____________

5. Many (has, have) watched movies about ancient Rome. ____________

Write the pronoun in parentheses that correctly completes each sentence.

6. (Nobody, Several) loves to study the history of money more than Maria.

____

7. (You, She) know a collector who buys rare coins on the Internet. ____________

8. (Each, Few) knows that the Bank of North America was the first U.S. bank.

____

9. (We, He) hopes to find a rare Hebrew coin at the coin shop. ____________

10. (Both, Nobody) use pocket calculators to balance their checkbooks. ____________

/10

Pronouns, Verbs, and Titles

A verb must agree with its subject pronoun.

Pronouns	**Verbs**
He, she, it	walks, is, was, has
We, you, they	walk, are, were, have
I	walk, am, was, have

Mechanics

- Underline or use italics for titles of books, plays, newspapers, magazines, movies, and TV series.
- Put quotation marks around titles of poems, short stories, essays, songs, articles, and book chapters.

Write each sentence correctly.

1. When traveling, I often read the newspaper USA Today.

____

____

2. The book on the table is A Woman's Guide to Investing.

____

____

3. My sister wrote a book called Investing in the Stock Market Today.

____

____

4. Everyone in the family watch the television show Wall Street Week.

____

____

Pronouns

Read the passage. Circle the letter of the word that belongs in each space.

> Ruben said, "Shameka and I ___(1)___ for the school paper *Pen, Pencil, and Keyboard.* It is very popular. I'm sure you ___(2)___ heard of it." Ruben paused. Then he added, "Many pick up ___(3)___ copy in the library."

1. **A.** write
   B. writes
   C. written
   D. writing
2. **F.** has
   G. had
   H. hasn't
   J. have
3. **A.** they're
   B. their
   C. there
   D. them

> Lisa told ___(4)___ that she lost her essay "A Ride on Pegasus." She asked, "If you and Kate find my paper, will you give ___(5)___ to me?" She looked concerned. I replied, "Of course. Do you want ___(6)___ to help you look for the assignment?"

4. **A.** Rosey and me
   B. me and Rosey
   C. Rosey and I
   D. I and Rosey
5. **F.** her
   G. them
   H. it
   J. him
6. **A.** we
   B. they
   C. us
   D. he

Pronouns

Read the sentences below. What is the antecedent for each underlined pronoun? Circle the letter of your answer.

> Casey needed to talk to Phil, so <u>she</u> (7) called him on the phone. Paw Paw and she wanted to know if he would drive <u>them</u> (8) to the market. Phil agreed and said they could ride with <u>him</u> (9) the next day.

7. A. Casey
B. needed
C. so
D. phone

8. F. if
G. market
H. wanted
J. Paw Paw and she

9. A. agreed
B. Phil
C. with
D. they

Read the sentences below. What form of pronoun is each underlined word?

> <u>I</u> (10) cannot find <u>my</u> (11) pencil. I will ask Tom if I may borrow <u>his</u> (12). If not, I'll ask someone else to lend me one.

10. A. Subject pronoun
B. Indefinite pronoun
C. Possessive pronoun
D. Object pronoun

11. F. Indefinite pronoun
G. Object pronoun
H. Possessive pronoun
J. Subject pronoun

12. A. Possessive pronoun
B. Object pronoun
C. Indefinite pronoun
D. Subject pronoun

Name ______________________ Date ____________

Adverbs

- An **adverb** is a word that modifies a verb, an adjective, or another adverb.
- An adverb can tell how, when, or where an action takes place.

Circle each adverb in the sentences below.

1. Nelson Mandela greeted the voters happily.
2. Chief Joyi eats his dinner late.
3. The cool breeze wafted gently across the meadow.
4. We saw a detour sign ahead.
5. Today, we go to Johannesburg.
6. Justice slammed the phone down angrily.
7. Oliver hurriedly cleaned his law office.
8. The children had left their toys everywhere.
9. The candidate will give a speech soon.
10. The soccer players jumped gleefully into the air.
11. The market place is located nearby.
12. Nelson and his advisors talked seriously.

Extension: Have the students draw an arrow from the adverb to the verb it modifies in the above sentences.

Modifying Adjectives and Adverbs

- **Adverbs** that modify adjectives and adverbs answer the questions *how?* and *to what extent*?

Read each sentence. Then underline each adverb that describes an adjective or another adverb. Next, in the blank, write the adjective or adverb being modified.

1. Mandela answered his letters quite promptly. ____________
2. The increasingly hostile crowd began to protest. ____________
3. The very costly construction project was finished. ____________
4. The telephone lineman climbed surprisingly high. ____________
5. Anna Lee's overly dangerous driving nearly caused an accident. ____________
6. The unbelievably happy woman accepted her first prize award. ____________
7. We painted the house too quickly. ____________
8. The traffic on the road was fairly quiet. ____________
9. South Africa's soccer team played exceptionally well. ____________
10. "I feel completely worn out," said Thembi. ____________
11. The suddenly silent audience paid close attention to Nelson. ____________
12. He spoke so loudly that everyone in the audience heard him. ____________

Extension: Have students write ten sentences using adverbs that modify adjectives or other adverbs.

Using Adverbs

- An **adverb** is a word that modifies a verb, an adjective, or another adverb.
- An **adverb** can tell how, when, or where an action takes place.
- **Adverbs** that modify adjectives and adverbs answer the questions *how?* and *to what extent*?

Read each sentence. Then fill in the blank with an adverb that tells how the action takes place.

1. Four men in khaki ____________ ransacked the Mandela home.
2. The men spoke ____________ to the children.
3. They ground their dirty boots ____________ into the living room rug.
4. Nelson Mandela spoke ____________ to his wife and son.
5. The men behaved ____________.

Read each sentence. Then fill in the blank with an adverb that tells when or where the action takes place.

6. The men opened the door and walked ____________.
7. They came ____________ from the street.
8. The men ____________ took Mandela from his home.
9. They said Mandela would not be back ____________.
10. His family wants to see him ____________.

Extension: Have students work in teams to write sentences using adverbs that tell *how*, *when*, and *where*.

Name ______________________ Date ____________

Using *Good* and *Well*

- *Good* is an adjective and is used to describe nouns.
- *Well* is an adverb that tells *how* about a verb.
- When *well* means "healthy," it is used as an adjective.

Read each sentence. Then fill in the blank using *good* or *well* correctly.

1. Nelson worked for a __________ law firm in the daytime.

2. He learned the law __________ and soon opened his own firm.

3. After visiting her village, you can __________ imagine the child's hardship.

4. Schools could not offer their students a __________ education.

5. Many of the schoolchildren could not learn __________.

6. "Are you feeling __________?" asked the teacher.

7. Mandela thought that laws requiring "pass books" were not __________ laws.

8. Johannesburg was not a __________ place to live for all people.

9. Police checked their identification __________.

10. The Africans behaved __________ in front of the judge.

Extension: Have students write a friendly letter in which they correctly use the words *good* and *well.*

Adverbs

Circle the adverb in each of the following sentences. Write *how* if the adverb tells how, *when* if the adverb tells when, or *where* if the adverb tells where the action takes place.

1. Nelson thought black South Africans were treated unfairly. ____________

2. The government should do something to improve their condition immediately.

   ____

3. He willingly attended rallies to protest the government laws. ____________

4. Mandela said, "Inequality does not belong here!" ____________

5. Soon people of all color were showing Mandela their support. ____________

6. People everywhere in the world voiced their concern. ____________

Circle the adverb in each of the following sentences. On the line provided, write the word the adverb modifies.

7. The government continually passed new laws that separated the people.

   ____

8. South Africans were angry about laws that created grossly inferior schools.

   ____

9. The number of protesters in the country grew steadily. ____________

10. People quite readily joined organizations like the African National Congress.

    ____

11. Nelson Mandela became an extremely strong leader in the ANC. ____________

12. He spoke in favor of a more democratic government. ____________

Working With Adverbs

- An **adverb** is a word that modifies a verb, an adjective, or another adverb.
- An **adverb** can tell how, when, or where an action takes place.
- **Adverbs** that modify adjectives and adverbs answer the questions *how?* and *to what extent?*

Mechanics

- *Good* is an adjective and is used to describe nouns.
- *Well* is an adverb that tells *how* about a verb.
- When *well* means "healthy," it is used as an adjective.

The author of this letter didn't check it over for mistakes. As you read the letter, correct the errors the writer made when using *good* and *well*. Then circle all of the adverbs in the letter.

3498 Penn Street

Westminster, CA 92683

February 17, 2000

Dear Alexander,

How is it going? I really hope you are feeling good, because recently I heard you took a very nasty fall on your bicycle. Will you recover quickly?

Tomorrow I will gladly bring you Tuesday's homework. Mrs. Chou read a truly interesting story about Nelson Mandela, and all of the students thought it was well, too. Mr. Mandela fought hard for the rights of the South African people. We talked enthusiastically about Mandela's life. The discussion went well. Mrs. Chou smiled broadly as we eagerly gave our opinions.

I will talk further with you when I see you.

Sincerely,

Julio

Adverbs That Compare

- The **comparative** form of an adverb compares two actions.
- The **superlative** form of an adverb compares more than two actions.
- For all one-syllable and some two-syllable adverbs, add *-er* or *-est* to form the comparative or superlative.

Write the comparative and superlative forms of each of the following adverbs.

	Comparative	Superlative
1. far	____________	____________
2. hard	____________	____________
3. long	____________	____________
4. near	____________	____________

Write each sentence using the comparative or superlative form of the following adverbs in parentheses.

5. Kennie rode Flicka (soon) than Kate rode Bright Star.

____

6. Flicka runs (fast) than Doughboy.

____

7. The stable owner bought Marigold (late) of those she purchased last year.

____

8. Kennie jumps her horse (high) of the five competing riders.

____

Extension: Have students write a paragraph in which they compare and contrast Flicka with another animal. Ask them to describe how they look and behave. Tell them to include at least five adverbs that compare.

Using *More* and *Most*

- For adverbs that end in *-ly* and most other adverbs with two or more syllables, use *more* to form the comparative and *most* to form the superlative.
- When you use *more* or *most*, do not use the ending *-er* or *-est*.

Write the comparative and superlative forms of each of the following adverbs.

	Comparative	Superlative
1. wildly	____________	____________
2. weakly	____________	____________
3. naturally	____________	____________
4. suddenly	____________	____________

Each sentence below contains an incorrectly formed adverb in parentheses. Circle the correct adverb.

5. Flicka's mane shines (radientlyest, most radiantly) in the sunlight.

6. She can ride her horse (most skillfully, more skillfully) than her friend.

7. The mare trots (awkwardlier, most awkwardly) in the meadow.

8. The bay horse neighs (most obnoxiously, more obnoxiously) than the Appaloosa horse.

Extension: Have students identify the comparative and superlative form of the adverbs in the above sentences.

Identifying Adverbs

- The **comparative** form of an adverb compares two actions.
- The **superlative** form of an adverb compares more than two actions.
- For all one-syllable and some two-syllable adverbs, add *-er* or *-est* to form the comparative or superlative.
- For adverbs that end in *-ly* and most other adverbs with two or more syllables, use *more* to form the comparative and *most* to form the superlative.
- When you use *more* or *most*, do not use the ending *-er* or *-est*.

Each sentence below includes an incorrectly formed adverb in the parentheses. Choose the correct form and rewrite the sentence on the line provided.

1. Kennie said, "Flicka canters (more gracefully, most gracefully) of all the horses I've ridden."

   ____

2. The Arabian horse can gallop (longest, most longly) in an open field.

   ____

3. Flicka crosses the stream (more eagerly, eagerlier) than the dog.

   ____

4. Joon Yang smiles (most pleasantly, pleasantliest) when riding at dawn.

   ____

5. The farmer ran (hurriedlier, more hurriedly) to the barn when it began to rain.

   ____

6. The three friends grinned (more happily, happilyer) at their parents.

   ____

7. The trainer yelled (most forcefully, most forcefulliest) at the bronco.

   ____

8. Today the fair was (more heavily, most heavily) attended than Saturday.

   ____

Extension: Have students write a journal topic using various forms of comparative and superlative adverbs. You might suggest they write about a pet or life on a horse farm.

Using Adverb Forms

- Some adverbs have irregular forms.
- The comparative and superlative forms of *well* are *better* and *best.*
- The comparative and superlative forms of *badly* are *worse* and *worst.*
- Never use *more* or *most* with irregular forms.

Complete each sentence below by writing the comparative form of the adverb shown in parentheses.

1. The Tennessee Walking Horse meeting in April was (well) ____________ attended than the horse race Sheila went to last week.
2. The dirt road to the stable was flooded (badly) ____________ than it had been after the last storm.
3. However, the horses were (well) ____________ trained at the Tennessee Walking Horse meeting than at last week's horse race.
4. This year's hurricane affected attendance (badly) ____________ than last year's storm did.

Complete each sentence below by writing the superlative form of the adverb shown in parentheses.

5. White Knight is the (well) ____________ known horse of all the horses in the show.
6. Of all his characteristics, people remember him (well) ____________ for his stubbornness.
7. No doubt, he can be the (badly) ____________ behaved of all the horses.
8. This year, his trainer will not be the (badly) ____________ prepared.

Extension: Have students write four more sentences using the comparative and superlative forms of *well* and *badly.*

Adverbs

Read each of the following sentences. Is there a mistake with the comparative adverb? Circle the letter of your response.

1. Lamont raced Flicka nearly the fence than was necessary.
   a. Change *nearly* to *nearer.*
   b. Change *nearly* to *nearliest.*
   c. Change *nearly* to *more nearer.*
   d. Make no change.

2. The child behaved gooder after he took a nap.
   a. Change *gooder* to *bester.*
   b. Change gooder to *more gooder.*
   c. Change *gooder* to *better.*
   d. Make no change.

3. We altered our route slighter after looking at the map again.
   a. Change *slighter* to *more slighter.*
   b. Change *slighter* to *slightly.*
   c. Change *slighter* to *slightest.*
   d. Make no change.

4. The sun shines more brightly at noon than at dusk.
   a. Change *more* to *most.*
   b. Change *brightly* to *brighter.*
   c. Change *more brightly* to *brightlier.*
   d. Make no change.

Read each of the following sentences. Is there a mistake with the superlative adverb? Circle the letter of your response.

5. The mare performed the worser of the three horses galloping.
   a. Change *three* to *other.*
   b. Change *worser* to *worst.*
   c. Change *worser* to *worse.*
   d. Make no change.

6. Jamie sauntered casuallyier to the fence post and waited.
   a. Change *casuallyier* to *most casually.*
   b. Change *casuallyier* to *casualyiest.*
   c. Change *casuallyier* to *more casuallyier.*
   d. Make no change.

Practicing Adverbs and Their Irregular Forms

- The **comparative** form of an adverb compares two actions.
- The **superlative** form of an adverb compares more than two actions.
- For all one-syllable and some two-syllable adverbs, add *-er* or *-est* to form the comparative or superlative.
- For adverbs that end in *-ly* and most other adverbs with two or more syllables, use *more* to form the comparative and *most* to form the superlative.
- When you use *more* or *most,* do not use the ending *-er* or *-est.*

Mechanics

- Some adverbs have irregular forms.
- The comparative and superlative forms of *well* are *better* and *best.*
- The comparative and superlative forms of *badly* are *worse* and *worst.*
- Never use *more* or *most* with irregular forms.

Read each sentence aloud. Choose the correct comparative adverb in parentheses. Write the sentence in the space provided.

1. I think (clearliest, more clearly) after a healthy breakfast.

____

2. Yesterday in training, Flicka pranced (badder, worse) than we expected.

____

3. Hector speaks (highlier, more highly) of your skill than Melissa's.

____

Read each sentence aloud. Choose the correct superlative adverb in parentheses. Write the sentence in the space provided.

4. The horse van runs (most smoothly, smoothliest) after its tune-up.

____

5. Susan felt (baddest, worst) after her last flu.

____

6. The competition rider (most perfectly, perfectest) rounded the barrel.

____

Negatives

- A **negative** is a word that means "no," such as *not, never, nobody, nowhere,* and contractions with *n't.*
- A **double negative** is an error in which two negatives are used together.
- You can correct a double negative by removing one negative.

Circle each negative in the sentences below.

1. The marathon runners have no more energy to finish the race.

2. The boys had not realized how long the competition would last.

3. None of them expected it to take so long.

4. The runners will never sign up for such a race again.

5. "I can't believe we lasted this long!" cried Marcus.

Each sentence below contains a double negative. Circle the negative words and correctly rewrite the sentence by removing one negative.

6. No Macedonians did not want to live in their war-torn land any longer.

____

7. They didn't want to be threatened by no soldiers.

____

8. If they left their village, they might not never see their families again.

____

9. These Macedonians could not depend on no one.

____

10. However, they can't no longer feel safe in their homes.

____

/10

Extension: Have students create five sentences containing double negatives. Then have them exchange papers and correct them.

Name ______________________ Date ______________ LEARN AND PRACTICE **Grammar** 174

More Double Negatives

- You can correct a double negative by replacing one negative with a positive word.

Read each sentence. If the sentence contains a double negative, rewrite it correctly. If the sentence is correct, write C on the line.

1. Alexander the Great was born in Macedonia and not in Greece.

____

2. He was taught by Aristotle, who wasn't no easy teacher.

____

3. Aristotle couldn't never find a better student than Alexander.

____

4. Alexander wasn't sorry he studied philosophy and medicine.

____

5. Many children didn't never have the opportunity to attend school.

____

6. Nobody learned about computers in Alexander's time.

____

7. No philosophers overlooked Alexander's remarkable military skill.

____

8. Alexander's military force wasn't nothing to ignore.

____

Extension: Have students identify the positive words in their corrected sentences.

Avoiding Double Negatives

- A **negative** is a word that means "no," such as *not, never, nobody, nowhere,* and contractions with *n't.*
- A **double negative** is an error in which two negatives are used together.
- You can correct a double negative by removing one negative.
- You can correct a double negative by replacing one negative with a positive word.

Rewrite each sentence below so that it does not contain a double negative.

1. The dealer would never let no one mount his horse Bucephalus.

____

2. No Greek or Macedonian couldn't ride the angry horse.

____

3. Alexander didn't want to lose the horse because nobody had no ability to ride it.

____

4. Bucephalus had never encountered no rider like Alexander before.

____

5. We will never know if the story of Alexander and Bucephalus is not true.

____

6. Some people thought Alexander would learn more if he didn't have no strict tutor.

____

7. Alexander didn't never become a philosopher like Plato.

____

8. Diogenes believed nothing mattered to nobody except a person's soul.

____

Extension: Have students write five sentences with one negative word in each.

Capitalization

- Capitalize proper nouns, such as names of people, cities, states, countries, geographical features, buildings, monuments, languages, and nationalities.
- Capitalize titles of people before names.
- Capitalize proper adjectives.

Correct any misused proper nouns, titles, and proper adjectives in the following sentences. Write your answer on the line provided.

1. Alexander's forces crossed the tigris river to reach the arabian sea.

____

2. One of the most famous monuments in greece is the parthenon.

____

3. The city of alexandria was named after alexander.

____

4. Troops quickly entered the greek city of athens.

____

5. Alexander's military conquests included much of asia minor.

____

6. "Can you find troy on the map?" asked king Philip.

____

7. Alexander married a persian woman and adopted many of her cultural ways.

____

8. After his death, a new culture called the hellenistic civilization developed.

____

9. Soldiers faced a grueling march across the hindu kush mountains.

____

10. Aristotle began a school called the lyceum.

____

Extension: Have students imagine they are taking a vacation. Have them write a descriptive letter to a friend using proper nouns, titles, and proper adjectives.

Name ______________________ Date ____________ TEST **Grammar** 177

Negatives

Each sentence below contains a double negative. Rewrite the sentence correctly.

1. The young boy didn't have no disrespect for Alexander's troops.

   ____

2. Not no person in the village grew unhappy when his soldiers entered town.

   ____

3. No one nowhere in this small town had traveled far from the area.

   ____

4. It didn't take no time for the news to spread.

   ____

5. "You shouldn't not miss seeing the troops!" cried the girl.

   ____

6. There wasn't no reason to fear Alexander's men.

   ____

7. No person did not want to see the troops.

   ____

8. The soldiers looked for extra food but couldn't find none.

   ____

9. The villagers didn't have nothing to offer the hungry men.

   ____

10. They hadn't never been prepared for this event.

    ____

___ / 10

Practicing Adverbs and Negatives

- A negative is a word that means "no," such as *not, never, nobody, nowhere,* and contractions with *n't.*
- A double negative is an error in which two negatives are used together.
- You can correct a double negative by removing one negative.
- You can correct a double negative by replacing one negative with a positive word.

Mechanics

- Capitalize proper nouns, such as names of people, cities, states, countries, geographical features, buildings, monuments, languages, and nationalities.
- Capitalize titles of people before names.
- Capitalize proper adjectives.

Rewrite each sentence, correcting the double negatives. Write the sentence with the correct capital letters.

1. alexander's teacher was not no general.

____

2. alexander was a king; he wasn't no poor man.

____

3. Some people disliked alexander because he wasn't no greek.

____

4. alexander didn't not become angry.

____

5. alexander wasn't no philosopher, but he was very eager to learn.

____

Prepositions

- A **preposition** comes before a noun or pronoun and relates that noun or pronoun to another word in a sentence.
- Common prepositions are *about, above, across, after, around, at, before, behind, below, between, down, for, from, in, near, of, on, over, to, with.*

Circle the preposition in each of the following sentences.

1. Roberto helped pack the car full of boxes.

2. Papa tied Mama's mattress to the car roof.

3. Mama kept a pot from the army surplus store.

4. She carried her big pot to the car.

5. Papa and Roberto helped Mama with her prized possession.

6. Papa crammed several boxes behind the front seat.

7. After the boxes, he packed more luggage.

8. Roberto placed a ball between two bags.

9. He found his lunch under the car seat.

10. Waiting in the car, Roberto ate his sandwich.

11. They drove out of the driveway.

12. He felt a lump in his throat.

13. The young boy looked back for the last time.

14. The family later found work at the Sullivan camp.

15. The family got work for the whole season.

Extension: Have students write three sentences with six different prepositional phrases.

Working with Phrases and Objects

- A **prepositional phrase** is a group of words that begins with a preposition and ends with a noun or pronoun.
- The **object of a preposition** is the noun or pronoun that follows the preposition.
- The verb must agree with the subject, not with the object of a preposition.

Read each sentence below. Underline each prepositional phrase, and circle the object of the preposition.

1. The family found life on the farm difficult.

2. They lived in a garage that was old and weather beaten.

3. Papa packed the wall holes with old newspapers.

4. Mama threw a worn blanket over the mattress.

5. The jacket he wore around his shoulders was tattered.

Circle the verb in the parentheses that correctly agrees with the subject. Then rewrite each sentence without the prepositional phrase.

6. The towel near the wash basin (belongs, belong) to Roberto.

____

7. The light without a bulb (needs, need) to be fixed.

____

8. The rules of the camp (are, is) important.

____

9. The sharecroppers on the Sullivan farm (were, was) hard workers.

____

10. The water in the jugs (refreshes, refresh) the thirsty laborers.

____

Extension: Have students circle the prepositions in the above sentences.

Reviewing Prepositions

- A **preposition** comes before a noun or pronoun and relates that noun or pronoun to another word in a sentence.
- Common prepositions are *about, above, across, after, around, at, before, behind, below, between, down, for, from, in, near, of, on, over, to, with.*
- A **prepositional phrase** is a group of words that begins with a preposition and ends with a noun or pronoun.
- The **object of a preposition** is the noun or pronoun that follows the preposition.
- The verb must agree with the subject, not with the object of a preposition.

Add a prepositional phrase that correctly completes the following sentences. Use the noun in parentheses as the object of the preposition. Rewrite each sentence on the line provided.

1. Several _____ rest next to the tree. (workers)

____

2. Roberto, Papa, and I walk _____. (field)

____

3. The sharecroppers threw the grapes _____. (basket)

____

4. When the school bus passed by, they hid _____. (vineyards)

____

5. They sat _____ to eat dinner. (table)

____

Circle the subject or verb in parentheses that correctly completes each sentence.

6. The opportunity for future jobs (depends, depend) on a healthy crop.

7. The (laborers, laborer) in the field arrive every day at 6 in the morning.

8. Each of the family members (have, has) a job to do.

9. The (box, boxes) in the truck are packed with grapes.

10. The grapes on the vine (are, is) ripe.

Extension: Have students write ten sentences, each with at least one prepositional phrase. Have them underline the prepositional phrases.

Punctuating Prepositional Phrases

- A prepositional phrase may come at the beginning of a sentence.
- Put a comma after a prepositional phrase composed of four or more words that comes at the beginning of a sentence.

Read the following sentences. Place a comma after the prepositional phrase if it is needed. If a comma is not needed, write **Correct** in the space provided.

1. Above the cliff flew a flock of ebony crows.

____

2. Across the pickup truck the sharecroppers strapped a tent.

____

3. The boy said, "I grew tired at the sight of packed bags."

____

4. Around the glowing campfire the women had placed a ring of rocks.

____

5. Without a single thought the boy ran quickly after the jackrabbit.

____

6. Down the worn path Mama saw a hungry coyote.

____

7. From life as a migrant a person can learn how to survive.

____

8. In the dark the owl peered knowingly at Roberto and Papa.

____

9. The author lived the life of a migrant farm worker.

____

10. Under the walnut tree a small child played with a straw doll.

____

Extension: Have students write six sentences that begin with prepositional phrases of various lengths. Have them use commas where necessary.

Prepositions

Identify the object of the preposition in each of the following sentences. Circle the letter of your choice.

1. The family arrived at the old farm and entered the driveway.

a. old
b. family
c. farm
d. at

2. The Sullivan's had plenty of hard work and gave them jobs.

a. work
b. them
c. plenty
d. of

3. The woman hung a woven basket above the open doorway.

a. basket
b. doorway
c. several
d. hung

Read each of the following sentences. Is there a mistake? Circle the letter of your response.

4. Around six o'clock the foreman calls the men in from the fields.

a. Add a comma after *o'clock.*
b. Change *foreman* to *foremen.*
c. Change *calls* to *call.*
d. Correct

5. Over the dusty chalkboard the teacher hangs several posters.

a. Change *teacher* to *teachers*.
b. Add a comma after *chalkboard.*
c. Change *chalkboard* to *chalkboards.*
d. Change nothing.

Practicing Prepositions and Prepositional Phrases

- A **preposition** comes before a noun or pronoun and relates that noun or pronoun to another word in a sentence.
- Common prepositions are *about, above, across, after, around, at, before, behind, below, between, down, for, from, in, near, of, on, over, to, with.*
- A **prepositional phrase** is a group of words that begins with a preposition and ends with a noun or pronoun.

Mechanics

- A prepositional phrase may come at the beginning of a sentence.
- Put a comma after a prepositional phrase composed of four or more words that comes at the beginning of a sentence.
- The **object of a preposition** is the noun or pronoun that follows the preposition.
- The verb must agree with the subject, not with the object of a preposition.

Read each sentence aloud. Then change the verb so that it agrees with the subject of the sentence. Rewrite each sentence on the line provided. Then add commas after prepositional phrases if they are necessary.

1. After sunset members of the work team heads back to the Sullivan farm.

____

2. Behind a huge packing crate a child of two play quietly by herself.

____

3. A number of grapes falls from the grapevine into the mud.

____

4. Around the sharp corner a jalopy swerve from its heavy load.

____

Sentence Combining

- Two sentences can be combined by adding an adjective or adverb to one sentence.

Read each pair of sentences. Combine the two sentences into one sentence, and write it on the line below.

1. Farmer Wang Zuolu lived next to the Yangtze River. The Yangtze River is beautiful.

____

2. His family lived in a house built by his great-grandfather. The house was built near the river.

____

3. Now Wang's life has changed. His life has changed forever.

____

4. The Yangtze is in the center of China. It is a long river.

____

5. China is building the largest dam in the world. It will be the most powerful in the world.

____

6. The Three Gorges Dam will be finished by 2009. It will be completely finished.

____

7. The $24 billion dam is important to the Chinese government. It is very important.

____

8. Many want to change China's main source of energy. They want to change it someday.

____

9. Some scientists think the dam will be a disaster. It will be an ecological disaster.

____

10. Clouded leopards may lose their home. The clouded leopards are rare.

____

Extension: Have students circle the adjectives and adverbs in the sentences above.

Combining Sentences

- Two sentences can be combined by adding a prepositional phrase to one sentence.

Read each of the sentence pairs. What is the best way to combine the two sentences into one sentence? Circle the letter of your answer.

1. Wang and his wife will find a new home. The home will be in a different city.
   - **a.** Wang and his wife will find a new home in a city.
   - **b.** Wang and his wife will find a new home in a different city.
   - **c.** Wang and his wife will find a different city and a new home.
   - **d.** Wang and his wife's home will be new and different.

2. The Chinese government promises to preserve a protective area. The area is for the dolphins.
   - **a.** The Chinese government promises to preserve a protective area, which is an area and it is for the dolphins.
   - **b.** An area for the dolphins is promised by the government to preserve the protective area.
   - **c.** The Chinese government promises to preserve a protective area for the dolphins.
   - **d.** For the dolphin area, the Chinese government promises to preserve a protective area.

3. Burning coal is China's main source of energy. Burning coal is bad for the environment.
   - **a.** China's main source of energy is bad for the environment.
   - **b.** Burning coal is bad for the environment and China's main source of energy.
   - **c.** Burning coal is bad for the environment and energy.
   - **d.** China's main source of energy is burning coal, which is bad for the environment.

4. Many of the areas near the Yangtze River are used for farming. The dam will destroy many of the areas used for farming.
   - **a.** The dam will destroy many of the areas near the Yangtze River that are used for farming.
   - **b.** Many of the areas near the Yangtze river will be used for farming and destroyed by the dam.
   - **c.** Many of the areas destroyed by the dam will be used for farming.
   - **d.** The farming by the Yangtze River will destroy the areas near the dam.

Extension: Have students ask a partner why the other combinations to the above sentence pairs are not the best way to combine the two sentences.

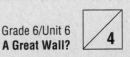

Using Sentence Combination

- Two sentences can be combined by adding an adjective or adverb to one sentence.
- Two sentences can be combined by adding a prepositional phrase to one sentence.

Read each pair of sentences. Combine the two sentences into one sentence and write it on the line below.

1. Poets write about the cliffs and plains along the Yangtze River. It has steep cliffs and flat plains.

   ____

2. Farmer Zuolu grew oranges and peanuts. He grew them on his farm.

   ____

3. Before they had to move, Wang's family lived peacefully. They had to move suddenly.

   ____

4. The dam's 607-foot high wall will span 1.3 miles. It will span 1.3 miles of the Yangtze River.

   ____

5. The project will alter the environment. The altered environment surrounds the dam.

   ____

6. Workers will move over 3.5 billion cubic feet of stone. Dam workers will also move earth.

   ____

Extension: Underline the prepositional phrases in the above sentences.

Commas

- Use a comma after an introductory word, such as *well.*
- Use commas to set off words that interrupt the flow of thought.
- Use commas to set off nouns of direct address and most appositives.
- Use a comma after a long introductory prepositional phrase.

Rewrite the sentences by inserting commas in the appropriate places.

1. Well I think it would be difficult to move so quickly.

____

2. "Dr. Chen what will happen to fish life in the river?" asked the reporter.

____

3. After the building of the dam the Chinese government will begin a new project.

____

4. The Three Gorges Dam which will be completed in 2009 will be awesome.

____

5. Sir may I introduce my mother?

____

6. Animals such as the dolphins may be endangered.

____

7. So would you like to live next to the Three Gorges Dam?

____

8. Preserving the natural environment is of course a primary concern of many.

____

9. Zhang Changying please address this letter to the pharmacist.

____

10. Before the dam's final completion many families will have relocated.

____

Extension: Write two sentences for each of the guidelines in the comma box above.

Sentence Combining

Read each pair of sentences. Combine the two sentences into one sentence using adjectives, adverbs, or prepositional phrases and then write it on the line below.

1. Wang's farm will be covered. It will be completely covered with water.

____

2. The family must move to another town. The town is far from the Yangtze River.

____

3. Families will move their homes. These homes will be on higher ground.

____

4. The dam will create a lake. The lake will be exceedingly deep.

____

5. The dam will protect the Chinese. It will protect them from river floods.

____

6. Since 1800 around 300,000 Chinese people have been killed. They have died from flooding.

____

7. The land surrounding the Three Gorges Dam will change. It will change drastically.

____

8. The scientists presented a model of the dam. The model was carefully constructed.

____

9. Wheels and magnets move generators. The generators are gigantic.

____

10. The dam is the Three Gorges Dam. Would you like to live near the dam?

____

/10

Practicing Sentence Combination

- Two sentences can be combined by adding an adjective or adverb to one sentence.
- Two sentences can be combined by adding a prepositional phrase to one sentence.

Mechanics

- Use a comma after an introductory word, such as *well.* Use commas to set off words that interrupt the flow of thought.
- Use commas to set off nouns of direct address and most appositives.
- Use a comma after a long introductory prepositional phrase.

Combine and revise each sentence pair about the picture into one sentence. Add commas if they are necessary. Write the sentence on the line provided.

1. China's Three Gorges Dam will provide hydroelectricity for millions of people. The hydroelectricity is vital.

____

2. The government believes hydroelectric power will improve living conditions. The conditions will greatly improve.

____

____

3. Coal burning which is China's main energy source is less efficient. It is less efficient than water power.

____

____

4. Among the people of China the dam is a topic of discussion. It is a hot topic.

____

Name ______________________________ Date ____________

Adverbs

Read the passage and look at each underlined adverb. What word does the adverb modify? Circle the letter of your answer.

> Alexander's military campaign was immediately (1) successful. He conquered the small town rapidly (2). Soon (3) people throughout the land heard the incredible news. Villagers seldom (4) forgot this young man's name.

1. **A.** successful
   B. military
   C. was
   D. campaign

2. **F.** rapidly
   G. conquered
   H. town
   J. small

3. **A.** land
   B. throughout
   C. incredible
   D. heard

4. **F.** forgot
   G. man's
   H. young
   J. name

Read the passage and look at the underlined sentences. Is there a mlstake? If there is, how do you correct it? Mark your answer.

> Nothing can't prepares John, the boy from town, for his horse ride today. (5) It's not going to be just another trip. For more than one hour he rapidly gallops Lady Lucinda across Daisy Meadow. (6)

5. **A.** Remove *can't.*
   B. Change *prepares* to *prepare.*
   C. Remove the comma after *town.*
   D. Make no change.

6. **F.** Change *Lady* to *lady.*
   G. Change *Meadow* to *meadow.*
   H. Add comma after *hour.*
   J. Make no change.

Adverbs

Read the passage and look at the underlined sentences. Is there a mistake? If there is, how do you correct it? Mark your answer choice.

> Well, the horse reacts more hesitant than John ever expected. (7) She quickly recovers. John is not no amateur rider, and both rider and horse dodge the Californian coyotes. (8) John's horse rides confidently off into the sunset.

7. **A.** Change *ever* to *never*.
   B. Change *hesitant* to *hesitantly*.
   C. Remove comma after *well*.
   D. Make no change.

8. **F.** Remove *not*.
   G. Change *Californian* to *californian*.
   H. Change *dodge* to *dodges*.
   J. Make no change.

Look at the sentence pairs. How could each pair best be combined? Mark your answer.

9. China's Three Gorges Dam is an ambitious construction project. The dam is on the Yangtze River.
   A. China's Three Gorges Dam is an ambitious construction project and is on the Yangtze River.
   B. An ambitious construction project on the Yangtze River is a dam called China's Three Gorges Dam.
   C. China's Three Gorges Dam, on the Yangtze River, is an ambitious construction project.
   D. The dam on the Yangtze River is China's Three Gorges Dam and an ambitious construction project.

10. It is a large construction project. It is the largest construction project since work began on the Great Wall.
    F. It is a construction project that is the largest since work began on the Great Wall.
    G. It is the largest construction project since work began on the Great Wall.
    H. It is a construction project that is large, the largest since work began on the Great Wall.
    J. Since work began on the Great Wall, it is the largest construction project.